THE RUNNER'S GUIDE

British Athletics

CollinsWillow

An Imprint of HarperCollins*Publishers*

First published in 1994 by
CollinsWillow
an imprint of HarperCollins*Publishers*
London

© HarperCollins*Publishers* 1994

A CIP catalogue for this book is
available from the British Library

ISBN 0 00 218462 1

Designed and produced by SP Creative Design
Linden House, Kings Road, Bury St Edmunds, Suffolk

Photographs by Mark Shearman
Art Director: Rolando Ugolini
Illustrations by Rolando Ugolini
Illustrations on pages 18 and 20 reference courtesy of Avia
Editor: Heather Thomas
Production: Fiona Connell-Finch

This is a new and completely revised edition of
the AAA Runner's Guide

Printed and bound in Great Britain by
Butler and Tanner Ltd, Frome, Somerset

Contents

Contributors

Sandra Dyson

Sandra Dyson, a former Great Britain International athlete, is a Chartered Physiotherapist running a busy practice in Cheshire, England, and specializes in sports injuries. She spent eleven years as Physiotherapist to the Great Britain Athletics Team and has accompanied the team to two Olympic Games, two Commonwealth Games and numerous international matches. She has recently produced a video tape on self-treatment of sports injuries.

Dr Yiannis (John) Koutedakis

Dr Yiannis Koutedakis has many years experience in researching and monitoring elite sports performance. He is a former International rower and British National Coach for Junior Rowing. In 1987 he was appointed Chief Physiologist at the British Olympic Medical Centre at Northwick Park Hospital in the UK. He is now a senior lecturer in sports physiology at Wolverhampton University, England, and the author of several scientific publications.

Dr Patrick Milroy

Dr Patrick Milroy is a general practitioner and Medical Advisor to the British Athletics Federation. He has been appointed doctor to the England Athletics Team for the 1994 Commonwealth Games and is also Medical Advisor to the UK magazine *Runner's World*.

Janet Pidcock

Janet Pidcock is a freelance writer covering nutrition and health subjects. A researcher for the North East Thames Regional Health Authority in the UK, she was also the nutrition consultant to *Running Magazine*. She is particularly interested in sports nutrition and writes regularly for a sports science journal.

Al Rockall

Al Rockall is a Founder-member of the Southern Counties Veterans Athletic Association, and a life-long runner. He ran for Highgate Harriers for over 20 years.

Steven Seaton

Steven Seaton is the Deputy Editor of *Runner's World* Magazine in the UK. He edits the annual shoe guide and all the specialist equipment features that appear in the magazine

Steve Smythe

Steve Smythe is a Staff Writer on *Runner's World* Magazine in the UK. He runs for Dulwich and has competed in over 1000 road races and cross-country races and has a marathon personal best of 2:29.

Sylvester Stein

Sylvester Stein is Vice President of the British Veterans Athletics Federation and a Contributing Editor to *Runner's World* Magazine in the UK. He is also Chairman of Sports and Leisure Magazines in the UK. An over-70s sprinter, he is the author of several books on fitness and running.

Cliff Temple

Cliff Temple was a British Amateur Athletic Board Senior Coach and *The Sunday Times* athletics correspondent until January 1994 when he died tragically. He will be missed and mourned by thousands of runners who have benefited over the years from his advice and have enjoyed reading his newspaper articles.

Bruce Tulloh

Bruce Tulloh was the European 5000m Champion in 1962 and a British International. He is now an active athletics coach, coaching several athletes including Richard Nerurkar, the World Cup Marathon Champion and English Cross-country Champion.

Harry Wilson

Harry Wilson has coached more than 80 international athletes, including Steve Ovett, the Olympic Champion and World Record Holder. Many of Harry's training routines, which have become accepted worldwide, were pioneered in conjunction with Ovett. He currently coaches a squad of athletes including some of Britain's best veterans and also a brilliant junior, Nikki Slater. He was the British National Event Coach for 800m and 1500m up until 1992. He is a lecturer and visiting coach at international conferences and training camps, and the author of several books on running and coaching.

Foreword

by Tony Ward, British Athletic Federation

Running has always been endemic to Man's existence. From prehistoric times, when speed and endurance must have been an essential ingredient for the hunter, through to the Greeks and their platonic ideals and the birth of the Olympic Games, to the running footmen of the Middle Ages and the pedestrianism of both men and women in the eighteenth and nineteenth centuries, we have always run. Firstly it was to maintain life itself; latterly it has become a life-sustaining recreation.

Men and women must have always competed because competition is innate to our nature. The day of the amateur dawned in 1880 in the Randolph Hotel in Oxford, England, when the Amateur Athletic Association was formed. One of the first great athletes of the new era was Walter George, the very first AAA 1 Mile Champion. He was an exceptional talent; so exceptional, in fact, that no amateur athlete could successfully compete with him. In 1886, running as a professional against his old rival Cummings, in west London, he set a time of 4 minutes 12³/₄ seconds. Nobody had come anywhere near such a time and it was to stand as a world best by an amateur or professional until Norman Taber of the USA beat it in 1915. No British athlete bettered it until 1935, when Sydney Wooderson ran a new British record, an amazing span of 49 years.

With the modern Olympics beginning in Athens in 1896 there came the marathon. Ever since that inaugural race, won by a Greek shepherd, Spyros Louis, men and women have been fascinated by the challenge of the marathon, and since the 1970s millions have run the distance in races from San Francisco to Beijing.

Today running is an accepted way of life and a drive into any town or city centre will see men and women of all shapes and sizes trying to get and keep fit. This book is especially for them, for those who aspire to fitness and health, who want to challenge themselves to, as Browning put it, exceed their grasp, to break a barrier, to win . . .

With such a line-up of experts making a contribution, even the experienced runner cannot fail to learn something from these pages. The Federation wishes you well, both in your reading and your running.

Getting started

by Al Rockall

The running revolution which started in the seventies and swept across Britain is here to stay. Far from being a fashionable craze or a passing phenomenon, running has grown into one of this country's most popular sports. The ever-growing popularity of running is borne out by the response of runners to the 1993 London Marathon, which had a field of 24,604 finishers and had to turn away another 45,000 hopefuls. Wherever you go, in city streets and parks, on country roads and fields, on riverbanks or along the beach, you will see people of all ages running.

Why do people run?

Well, there are many reasons:
- To lose weight
- To stay physically fit
- To stay youthful
- To reduce the risk of developing heart disease
- Simply because they enjoy it

For running is the ideal form of exercise: it's cheap – your only expense is kitting yourself out with a good pair of running shoes and a tracksuit; it's easy to master as you get fitter and train more frequently, as you need no special athletic ability; and it can be done anywhere at any time.

There are books that guarantee fitness in just 30 minutes a week. Don't believe it. To get really fit, you will have to work hard at your training and make a definite commitment to running. You cannot expect to excel at running immediately and it will take at least two months before you begin to feel like a fit and competent runner. During this time you can gradually build up your endurance and stamina as you build greater challenges into your personal fitness programme.

Some controversial views about the beneficial and detrimental effects of running on health have been expressed in the press, but generally, it is the people who are non-runners who claim that running may be harmful in certain circumstances. Most doctors agree that regular running can bring about:

- Low resting heart rate
- A drop in blood pressure
- A greater capacity to take in oxygen
- More efficient heart and lung action

This is because running is a truly aerobic form of exercise which helps strengthen the cardiovascular system (heart, lungs and the circulatory system) and makes your body process oxygen in a more efficient manner. This is referred to as the 'aerobic training effect'. Scientific studies carried

Test your fitness

To test how fit you are, try walking briskly for 20 minutes without stopping. If you are short of breath, dizzy or your legs ache, then you are very unfit indeed, and it might be a good idea to try walking before you start running and gradually build short bouts of running into your walking programme.

out in the United States have found that runners are less likely than non-runners to suffer from heart disease, and they have a higher stress-toleration threshold.

Experience better health

As a regular runner, your fitness will increase, your health will probably improve and you will reduce the risk of developing heart disease. Now even some postcardiac patients start running as part of their convalescent therapy. So running can be an all-round conditioner and play an important part in preventive medicine. It may help to reduce stress, worry and nervous tension as it has a pleasantly tranquillizing effect and is astonishingly therapeutic.

Control your weight

Running is also an excellent form of weight control, and regular training will make you slimmer as you can burn up to 1,000 calories per hour on a hard run. You can half-starve yourself on some trendy diet to lose weight quickly but the lost pounds will soon return if you do not continue to control your weight. Running is a far more effective weapon in losing and maintaining weight, whether you change your diet or not. When you run, you burn up unwanted surplus calories which the body otherwise converts into fat. Exercise can increase your metabolic rate so that you burn up calories faster.

Some people find that running actually depresses their appetite so that they feel less hungry and eat less. In any case, in your first year of running you can expect to lose about 10 pounds in weight. You will probably notice a large weight loss in the first few weeks but this will slow down steadily and eventually your weight will stabilize at what is best for you. This will depend on your weekly mileage total and your calorie intake. If you stop training regularly and burn up less calories, then you may find that you put on lost weight, and carrying extra weight will make a difference to your performance and running times when you start training again.

You can run at any age

Another great thing about running is that you are never to old to enjoy it, unlike many competitive contact sports such as football and rugby. Many committed runners continue running well into their sixties and seventies. They often look more youthful than non-runners a decade younger than themselves, and stay fit and agile.

Children, too, can enjoy running, and some families like to go out training together. Running is natural to children but lack of conditioning sometimes makes it difficult for adults and at first you may have to persevere until it comes naturally again.

Overcome your shyness

Some people secretly wish to take up running but they are afraid to do so for fear of looking foolish or being laughed at by their family, neighbours or friends – this is particularly true in the case of overweight people, who take up running to get slim. If you are shy or self-conscious, then avoid running on crowded streets and busy roads.

Another boost to your confidence and a good training method is to find a friend who wants to take up the sport and run together, providing each other with moral support. In this way, you can share the experience of running and motivate each other to succeed as a spirit of friendly rivalry develops and you give each other mutual encouragement. Some people find running on their own boring and prefer to run in company so that they can chat as they run along. Running regularly with friends increases the pressure on you not to miss a run whereas you might sometimes cry off if you always run by yourself.

At all levels, right from the beginning, running can be as individual or as competitive as you want it to be. You can compete against yourself, setting yourself new targets and goals, like getting fit and into shape or running five miles without stopping – it's entirely up to you. Only you

In your first fun run, don't get carried away at the start by going too fast. Settle in and pace yourself throughout and feel that you have something left at the end for next time.

can determine how to run, how far and how fast – unlike team sports, there are no set rules to govern your performance, which is under your own control. If you are naturally competitive, you may wish to join a club and compete against other runners as your running improves, either on the track, the road or cross-country. You just have to find your own level of competition.

Develop a training plan

When you start out, you should follow a running programme which is tailored to your own level of fitness and will fit into your lifestyle and daily pattern. Take care that the programme is not over-ambitious or you may not last the course. Follow our suggested starter programme (see page 16) and make a definite commitment to getting into shape.

In order to do this, you must set aside one hour for exercise on at least three days every week. You should not run for the duration of the hour. Spend 10-15 minutes warming up and stretching (see page 25) to ease out tense muscles and prevent post-run stiffness, about 15-20 minutes running (and walking at the beginning), and the remaining time spend cooling down and stretching and taking a bath or shower to take the sting out of tired muscles. As the weeks pass and your training programme progresses, the stiffness and laboured breathing will pass as a new level of fitness gradually sets in and your body responds more efficiently and feels lighter.

How do you start?

So, having decided that you want to start running for whatever reason, how do you go about it? First, you must take a good, long look at yourself and assess your physical condition. If you are heavily overweight or haven't exercised on a regular basis for a very long time, then it might even be a good idea to see your doctor and have a physical check-up before you start running.

This is particularly necessary if you smoke or drink heavily or have a family background of heart disease. Your doctor might tell you, of course, that you are mad to even want to run – this is a common reaction among some non-running doctors, and if this happens to you, then seek a second opinion from a doctor who does run. You must also consult the doctor if you experience chest pains or dizziness when you start running – there is probably a simple explanation but it is always just as well to check it out.

Do not be put off or dismayed by all this – most people are capable of starting a running programme and getting fit and there are very few who must not run for medical reasons. However, it is always wise to take precautions and seek advice if you have any doubts about your health.

When should you run?

Well, this depends entirely on your daily schedule. A lot has been written about the best time of the day and how it governs athletic performance. The only hard and fast rule is never to run immediately after eating – always allow at least two to three hours. It is also wise not to run in very hot or humid weather which could lead to heat stroke.

Try and choose a time of day that you can keep free for running and will enable you to establish a regular routine. Unless you run regularly (at least three times a week) you will not derive any benefits from it and fitness will remain both elusive and undiscovered. So right from the start, set aside an hour at a time that is convenient to you, and if you can stick to that time every day, then running will soon become an enjoyable habit which is hard to break.

Many people like to run at lunchtime from a local gym or a sports centre which has changing and showering facilities. However, if you often have working lunches or tend to to the shopping in your lunch hour, then choose another more convenient time of day. Always allocate enough time to change, warm-up and stretch, go for your run, cool down and shower or bathe afterwards.

Where should you run?

You can run anywhere – across the countryside, around your housing estate, a local park, along city pavements or even on the beach. Never start out by running on a local athletics track – not only is the special surface hard on your legs but lapping the same old track can be

The beauty of running is that you can run anywhere at any time. Wherever you travel, all you need take with you are your running shoes. You can run on the beach, in city parks or in the countryside.

Are you running at the right speed?

To discover whether you are running at the right speed, you can try the talk test. If you cannot hold a conversation with a friend without feeling winded and short of breath, then you are running too fast and should slow down. For most beginners, this means covering one mile in 10-12 minutes against 6 minutes for a more experienced athlete. You will find that your speed is affected by many factors – the time of day, your physical condition, the weather, the level of the ground and whether you are running uphill, downhill or on the flat.

incredibly boring after a while and your new-found enthusiasm for running will soon fade away.

To combat possible boredom, make sure that you choose several running routes which are interesting and present a variety of scenery for you to enjoy as you run along. Switch the routes around frequently so that you have new things to look at which will help distract you from any small muscular aches and pains that you may feel during the first few weeks.

Mix up your surfaces so that although you include a little road running in your training programme, you run on grass most of the time. Springy grass is less

jarring to legs, feet and back muscles than hard road surfaces and helps to cushion you against injury. Avoid running on ground that is uneven and riddled with potholes and hard tussocks of grass which could trip you up or throw you off stride. If the grass is very wet and slippery or the ground is soft and muddy, then wear running shoes with a special studded sole for gripping.

How often should you run?

You ought to run at least three times a week to make any progress and build up your level of physical fitness. Do not run on consecutive days in the early stages but have a day's rest between running days if possible. At first your body may feel stiff as you put it through unfamiliar exercises and ask it to perform new tasks. However, the stiffness should last for only a day and should be no more than a feeling of discomfort. If it is really painful and continues for several days then admit that you have been overdoing it and have run too far or too fast. Next time you train, decrease the distance and run more slowly.

Running is hard at the beginning until you start to feel more supple and relaxed and the first signs of fitness appear. Try to fit your run in regularly and do not look for excuses for missing training, especially when it is cold or wet outside. You can only build up fitness gradually through regular training, and until your body becomes really conditioned and running is an essential part of your life, it is easy to risk forfeiting the progress you have made and put your training back a week or two by missing a few days. Of course, this cannot be helped if you are ill – running with a heavy cold, flu or a virus infection is not recommended. Also, do not run if you are injured and in pain. If the injury persists for more than one week, seek medical advice.

How far and how fast should you run?

This will depend on your level of fitness and how inactive you used to be. The important thing is to build up distance gradually, starting with maybe only 100 yards or so and increasing the distance slowly as your running improves. If you start to feel tired or your breathing becomes laboured, then stop running and walk for a while until you feel better. You will soon be able to run further and walk less without feeling tired, and then you can think about increasing the distance, and extending your route.

Within a couple of months of regular training you should be able to run two or three miles without stopping. You will probably feel exhilarated and a marvellous sense of achievement at what you have accomplished. Never rush your training – this can lead to injury if you over-strain muscles that are more used to a sedentary existence. Be patient and build up your running time and distance gradually as

Measuring your pulse rate

This is a good method of checking up on how your body is responding during a run. Most adults have a resting pulse rate of 60-80 beats a minute but this increases when you run as your heart beats faster to pump the blood around the body. Take your pulse rate by pressing your wrist on the thumb side before you set out for your run, during the run and afterwards.

An easy way is to count for 15 seconds and then multiply by four to determine the rate per minute. Your pulse rate when you run should fall somewhere between your personal maximum and minimum permissible levels. To work out your maximum level deduct your age from 200; and to find the minimum level, subtract your age from 170.

Therefore if you are 40 years old, your pulse rate should lie in the 130-160 region. If it is less, then you are running too slowly. If it exceeds 160, then you are running too fast and should slow down. You will soon establish a pace that is right for you as you get more experienced as a runner, and after several months you may find that your pulse resting rate decreases as your heart grows stronger and more efficient.

your endurance and stamina increase. Run at a pace that is comfortable to you and get into a regular running rhythm. Initially, this will be just fractionally above a brisk walking pace, but as you get more proficient and the effort required to run decreases, you will certainly run faster. As your running improves you will take less time to cover your usual route and you will have to increase the distance to make up your usual allotted running time.

Running style

It is important to develop a relaxed, flowing running style to make running more enjoyable and reduce the risk of

Cross-country running in muddy conditions requires a special style, and it is important to keep your arms balanced and moving rhythmically.

injury. Running should come naturally and easily – do not run stiffly, pounding along with gritted teeth, tense shoulders, your arms punching the air as many new runners mistakenly do. Try to relax and let your body feel loose and easy when you run. Run erect and tall, not leaning forwards as this can cause back pain and put strain on leg muscles.

● **Your arms and shoulders** give you balance and the rhythm that keeps you going. So relax your shoulders and carry your arms low, moving in rhythm with your body. Your right arm balances the action of your left leg and vice versa. Never clench your fists as this increases tension and body strain. Keep your hands loose and relaxed.

● **Footstrike** is another aspect of running style and should always be light and rocking. There are basically three ways of contact between the foot and the ground. Most long-distance runners use the heel-to-toe technique, landing on the heel and then rocking forwards to the ball of the foot and pushing off from the toes. This is a good style to develop as it spreads out the pressure of the body and cushions your weight as you land.

A few runners are flat-footed and land on the whole foot. This obviously has a cushioning effect also but it can be tiring if carried out over long distances. The third technique, which is common among many women runners who wear high heels regularly, is to land on the ball of the foot and then roll back onto the heel for the

Running tip

A last word on running style and technique: many runners try so hard to relax that paradoxically they become self-conscious and tense in the process. The key to natural, easy running is to keep your body loose and fluid and, as you run more frequently and your body becomes more supple and your self-confidence increases, your running will naturally become more flowing.

push-off. This method often produces sore muscles as it puts a lot of strain on the legs.

You can check your foot alignment and decide which category you fit into by running in wet sand or mud and then analysing your footmarks. You can correct poor footstrike to some extent by using arch supports or special shoe inserts. These act as shock-absorbers when your foot hits the ground and may stop you pronating. Finding the right running shoes will also improve footstrike and prevent injury.

● **Stride length** When you run, take good strides. The most efficient stride is long and smooth and uses less effort than a short, uneven stride. Never over-stride by reaching out too far with your feet. You will achieve this by pushing the ground away behind you – *not* by reaching forward for it.

● **Breathing** It is quite permissible to breathe through your mouth and take great gulps of air when you are out running. Breathing daintily through your nose will not take in enough air to satisfy your body's oxygen needs. Breathe in a relaxed way, expanding your abdomen fully as you breathe in and flattening it as you exhale. In this way, you use your lungs more efficiently, inflating them to their limits. Let your breathing be in tune with the movement of your body and establish a rhythm for your running, so that your whole body moves in harmony.

Beginners' running programme

Many beginners find it easier to follow a specially designed running programme than to find the time and the self-discipline to devise their own schedule. This programme has been devised by John Hanscombe, an experienced runner.

Your first aim, if you have not run before, is to be able to run for 15 minutes three times a week. You will probably find that you cannot run non-stop for 15 minutes and will have to run and walk alternately until gradually you will find that you are running more and walking less. Distance is immaterial, but the run should always be of 15 minutes' duration, even if you have to walk every hundred yards or so. Try to run on soft ground in your local park or countryside, but if this is not practical then ignore your neighbours and simply open the front door and run and walk for 7½ minutes before turning back for home.

Over the first three or four weeks of following this programme, the amount of walking will gradually diminish and by the fifth week you will probably be able to run without stopping for the prescribed 15 minutes. If you find that you need an extra week or two to reach this goal, do not worry; patience and persistence are part of the build-up programme.

When you have overcome the first hurdle, lengthen your runs to 20 minutes three times a week, and at the weekends extend an outing to 30 minutes. Do not worry if you find that you have to walk occasionally, especially during the longer weekend run. Just keep going out four times a week until you are able to finish all of your runs without walking, no matter how slowly you seem to be going. After a further three or four weeks you should have reached this goal.

You are now ready for the next stage of the programme. You should be feeling much fitter and enjoying your running, which by now is an established part of your weekly routine. Now is the time to build up your running time and the distance covered, and possibly to join up with other runners on some occasions and run together. You will be surprised how much easier long runs become when you can share them with company. Soon you will be running five, and later six, days a week until you are feeling really fit.

At the end of this 12-week beginners' programme, you may be ready to enjoy running at club-level in cross-country and road events if you have a competitive streak, or you may prefer to go on running alone or with friends just for the fun and level of fitness it gives you.

Training programme

Weeks 1, 2, 3, 4

Run/walk for 15 minutes, 3 times a week until you can run 15 minutes non-stop

Weeks 5, 6, 7, 8

Weekdays: run/walk for 20 minutes, 3 times a week

Weekends: run/walk for 30 minutes on Saturday *or* Sunday

Keep this up until you can run non-stop for the times given above

Weeks 9, 10

Sunday	- very slow for 45 minutes, perhaps with occasional walk
Monday	- steady run for 20 minutes
Tuesday	- steady run for 30 minutes
Wednesday	- rest
Thursday	- run for 15-20 minutes at a brisk pace
Friday	- steady run for 20 minutes
Saturday	- rest

Weeks 11, 12

Sunday	- slow run for 45 minutes without walking
Monday	- steady run for 20 minutes
Tuesday	- steady run for 30 minutes
Wednesday	- steady run for 20 minutes
Thursday	- run hard for 15-20 minutes
Friday	- rest
Saturday	- steady run for 20-25 minutes

Running equipment

by Steven Seaton

The great appeal of running is its simplicity. You can do it almost anywhere, on your own and with a minimum of equipment. Or at least that is the way it seems. In theory it should be, but as soon as you graduate from the ranks of the once or twice a year recreational runner into a more committed practitioner, the need and desire for more specialist equipment arises.

Your first visit to a sports shop in search of the correct kit can be an intimidating experience: row after row of shoes designed for a range of feet, surfaces and budgets; racks of multi-coloured clothing; and a mind-boggling array of ancillary equipment.

If you can find a specialist running shop, it will always be your best option for advice, if not price. They are always staffed by runners, who understand the equipment they are selling and the problems you are likely to encounter.

This chapter will also help. It is designed to guide you through all the equipment you are likely to encounter and to arm you with the essential questions you need to ask yourself before you go to a shop, and the ones you must ask when you arrive.

The running shoe

A shoe is a shoe, is a shoe. Try running a marathon in a pair of tennis shoes and then see if you still believe that. Your shoes are without doubt the most important item of equipment in your running wardrobe. Basketball boots, cross-trainers or simple plimsolls will not stand up to the strain of running any regular distance, a point your feet and legs will quickly make clear to you.

Running shoes are designed specifically for the demands of the sport, but despite all the technical effort that goes into the design of running shoes, the best shoe is likely to be one that you don't notice. If you can train for and run a marathon without thinking about your shoes, without feeling any pain in the joints or without suffering a blister or blooded toe, then you have found the perfect shoe.

In most cases keeping the problems to a minimum is the best that most of us actually achieve. The repetitive forward motion of running puts great strain on your body. Your shoes are your first and best line of defence. In short, they are designed to minimize two things: shock and instability.

Busting the shoe jargon

Before you make your way to a shop to buy a new pair of shoes, it is important that you know what you are looking at and for.

It may seem like technical small talk, but having some rudimentary knowledge is crucial if you are going to make the correct choice and avoid an inappropriate pressure purchase.

Outsole

This is the part of the shoe that comes directly in contact with the ground. Its role is partly cushioning, and largely grip and durability. In most cases it is constructed from simple rubber or a more durable carbon rubber compound. Racing shoes, or those which are designed with more speed than distance in mind, have blown rubber outsoles, which are lighter and more cushioned but less durable.

Outsole patterns are seemingly infinite. If you run regularly off-road, then look for a wide-grip profile that will not clog-up easily with debris.

Midsole

Located between the outsole and the upper, this is the real heart of a running shoe. It is the area that provides most of the cushioning and the stability. Most midsoles use either Ethylene Vinyl Acetate (EVA), a polymer injected with air,

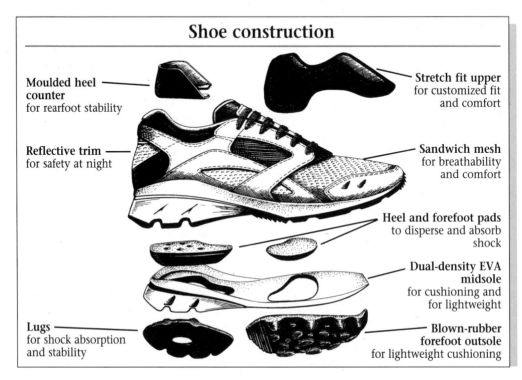

Shoe construction

Moulded heel counter
for rearfoot stability

Reflective trim
for safety at night

Lugs
for shock absorption and stability

Stretch fit upper
for customized fit and comfort

Sandwich mesh
for breathability and comfort

Heel and forefoot pads
to disperse and absorb shock

Dual-density EVA midsole
for cushioning and for lightweight

Blown-rubber forefoot outsole
for lightweight cushioning

Polyurethane (PU) or a manufacturer's version of the same. EVA is light, offers excellent cushioning but tends to break down quicker than PU. In contrast, PU lasts longer but is firmer and heavier than EVA. To improve durability EVA, is often compression moulded (heated up and subjected to pressure) or made in firmer densities with less air injected.

Midsole additions

The main marketing point in a shoe is not the basic midsole material, but the addition to the midsole to improve either cushioning, stability or both. A highly cushioned, resilient unit is inserted in the midsole at the point of heaviest impact, under the heel or the the forefoot. Each manufacturer makes its own claims for their technology and it is difficult, if not impossible, to prove scientifically which is the best.

Stability units are intended to prevent adverse movement of the foot, usually excessive inward rolling or pronation. Often this is achieved by putting firmer midsole materials on the inside of the shoe, or special plastic wedges or graphite plates in the same place.

Insole

The insole comes between your foot and the midsole. Traditionally its role was comfort, absorbing sweat, reducing blisters and providing a firm and comfortable base of support. While it still carries out that role, it is seen increasingly as an added layer of cushioning. A good insole can upgrade markedly the cushioning in an average shoe. Some runners insist on replacing the insole supplied with the shoe with one from a specialist manufacturer.

Upper

Although manufacturers are now marketing the idea of improved fit, with individual lacing systems or one piece stretch Neoprene and Lycra shells, the upper is really of only minimal importance to the road runner. Light weight, support and durability, particularly in the front toe box, are the main requirements. The midsole or outsole often wear out before the upper.

Heel counters and tabs

The heel counter is a piece of plastic which is moulded and wrapped internally around the heel. Its job is to prevent the rear of the foot moving inside the shoe. It should be firm to the touch, locked into the midsole and capable of preventing any sideways movement. Heel tabs, although designed to protect the Achilles tendon, often irritate if they are too firm or high. The lower and softer the tab the better.

Lasts and construction

Few runners know or care about the last of a shoe, but matching the correct one to your foot is the most important factor in determining comfort and fit.

The last is the metal or wooden shape the shoe is constructed around. It determines the basic shape of the shoe, its fit and support characteristics. Lasts for running shoes come in four basic shapes:

Straight Almost perfectly straight, this is the most supportive last and is preferred by runners who over-pronate.

Slightly curved This has a slight inflare, has good support on the inside of the shoe, but is less cumbersome than the straight last.

Semi-curved This is again more curved, has some support on the medial side, but is usually preferred by runners with a normal footstrike.

Curved This is the most curved, has no support on the inner side, but is considered the most responsive, flexible and mobile of the four basic types. Curved lasts are usually on racing shoes or lightweight trainers.

Running shoes are constructed in one of three ways: board, slip or combination lasting:

Board The upper is stretched over the last and glued to a flexible innersole board.

Board lasting provides good stability, but is relatively inflexible.

Slip The upper is stitched together underneath and slipped over the last. Slip lasting provides flexibility and lightness.

Combination This is a combination of the two. The shoe is board lasted at the rear for stability and slip lasted in the forefoot for flexibility.

Women's shoes

Conscious of the increasing number of women coming into the sport, companies now aggressively market specialist running shoes for women. The only real difference, however, is in the cosmetics and the fit. They are built on women's lasts which are narrower in the heel area. Most women would not have a great problem with a men's model in the correct size, particularly with the greater emphasis on fit in the upper.

Running shoe classsification

Making the right choice

Selecting the right shoe is a lot easier if you ask yourself the right questions. You need to consider your height, weight and the amount and type of running and racing you do. Think about the kind of surface you run on most often, your footshape and whether you over-pronate (the excessive inward rolling of your foot).

A post mortem on your last pair of training shoes will help to determine if you have any biomechanical problems. Put your old shoes on a flat surface and look at them from behind. Check for any lean in either direction; if the midsole leans inwards, it's odds on that you over-pronate, outwards and you over-supinate. Also look at the wear pattern of the outsole which will provide further clues.

Another alternative is to examine a wet footprint and check the shape of your foot and how high the arch is. Flat feet tend to over-pronate and require added support on the inside of the shoe. High arches are more rigid, tend to over-supinate (excessive outward rolling of the foot). Ask a running shoe specialist if you need orthotics or shoe inserts to correct the problem.

Buying guidelines

1 Select a reputable retailer, preferably one that specializes in running equipment.
2 Set a budget and stick to it before you go to the shop. You can easily spend a lot of money but the medium-priced range is as much as the vast majority will need.
3 Go in the afternoon. Your feet swell up during the day and will more closely resemble their running shape than first thing in the morning. Take along your running socks and try the two together.
4 Thoroughly check inside any model you select. Look for raised ridges or loose stitching which could irritate your feet.
5 Put on both shoes, run about the shop and ensure they fit properly when you are in motion. There should be a narrow space between the big toe and the end of the

inside of the shoe. Remember that if the shoes don't feel good in the shop, they won't feel good on the road.

Specialist shoes

Road shoes, as the name implies, are designed specifically for the road and, although suitable for occasional forays off-road, they are not up to regular encounters with cross-country courses. Alternatively, if you are likely to be one of the elite few at the head of the field, or race regularly on the track, then you need to think about investing in a pair of more specialist shoes.

Racing flats
These are shoes designed purely and simply for speed. If you don't have it you don't need them. They are built on a narrow curved last with a flat outsole profile.The majority of cushioning and stability devices in the midsole and outsole are dispensed with in the interests of weight reduction. As a rough guideline, if you run outside 2:45 for the marathon or 1:40 for the half, then you are not fast enough for racers. If you are over 11 stone, again you will need the cushioning more than the loss of weight. Wearing racing flats if you don't need them, won't make you a better athlete; they will make you injured. In any case, losing a kilo or two will make far more difference to your times than a few grams off your shoes.

Track spikes
Designed for the track or occasionally for grass training sessions, spikes also follow a

minimalist theory of design. A plastic or carbon spike plate, six or seven spikes, a rubber heel and a flimsy nylon and synthetic upper, is about all you can expect. Longer distance spikes (1500m and longer) have a thicker heel wedge than sprint spikes, but it is still negligible compared to a pair of road shoes. Unless you race regularly on the track, you will probably find a pair of racing flats better for long-distance track races, and because the upper is so flimsy, a track spike is not interchangeable with a cross-country spike. The length of spike permitted varies, but is usually no longer than 6mm.

Cross-country shoes and spikes

The difference between a specialist cross-country shoe and a road shoe is in the grip and the upper. In both cases the cross-country is far more demanding. The shoe has to provide traction on wet, muddy ground or grass and the upper has to withstand a battering in poor off-road conditions. Spikes have studded rearfoots and forefoot spike plates, with spike lengths interchangeable depending on the conditions. If you don't want spikes, choose a rubber studded outsole, similar to a fell shoe. The upper of both is usually thicker synthetic material which has some water repellence

Fell or mountain shoes

Compared to their road cousins, fell shoes look technically very basic, but your road shoes wouldn't last five minutes on the fells. Grip and durability are everything. Strong and lightweight synthetic uppers sit almost directly on top of a studded carbon rubber outsole. Don't expect much in the way of cushioning or added stability units; they are expensive unnecessary extras when coming down a mountain at speed.

Clothing

Compared to your feet, kitting out the rest of your body is a relatively straightforward affair. Although you will find specialist equipment for every body part or conceivable need, there is no reason why more general sports clothes can not, at least initially, double for running.

Vests and shorts

The basic summer racing outfit should be first and foremost comfortable. The most common material for shorts, which come with a built in gusset as standard, and vests is Coolmax, a material that is extremely good at transporting sweat away from your body. It is far better than ordinary nylon or cotton, which either prevent sweat from escaping or hold it in the material. Other materials similar to Coolmax have also recently entered the market to provide a wider choice. Look for well finished seams which will not chaff, and soft waistbands.

Another popular trend is to dispense with conventional running shorts in favour of longer legged Lycra shorts. They provide free well supported movement, particularly around the hamstrings, and prevent chaffing between the legs. On the down side, they tend not to be as good at taking away sweat and have to be worn with underwear underneath.

Socks

A shoe is often only as good as the sock inside it. A poor sock will make your life a misery; a good one will keep your feet dry and free of irritating foot blisters. In most cases, comfort, with good fit, is the key feature to worry about. Coolmax socks are good in the summer, but the move to two-layer socks with one layer transporting away perspiration, the other absorbing it, is a positive step for runners who suffer with blisters. As with other clothing, synthetic materials are better than cotton. Look out for prominent seams and make sure that socks fit snugly.

Bras

Finding a good supportive bra can be the difference for a woman between staying with the sport and leaving it. Look particularly for seamless cups, non-chaffing armholes and a broad supportive band below the cups which will not ride up. Some of the more common models are now Lycra, and cotton fully elasticated bras without any fastening. By removing clips and most of the seams, potential chaffing points are heavily reduced.

Keeping dry

It is not just a matter of keeping the rain out; it is also a question of letting perspiration escape. Cheap coated nylon jackets may keep the water out but they are hot and uncomfortable on long training runs. Unfortunately the jackets that are lightweight, waterproof and breathable, notably Gore-Tex, are expensive. Recently more fabrics which claim to have the same features have been introduced. Technically they are excellent but still an expensive option. For just warming up before a race a trilobal suit or even a shell suit will suffice; if you plan to run a lot in it, go for a microfibre fabric. Look for good back ventilation, reflective patches at front and back, pockets and long zips on the trousers to help you put them on without taking your shoes off.

Keeping warm

Staying warm conjures up a picture of several layers of heavy fleece clothing blocking out the cold. While it does keep you warm, such an outfit is heavy, it makes your sweat a lot and doesn't let your body breathe. On a long run the sweat cools and instead of staying warm you are often cold. Modern thermal tops are feather light, insulate your body, but breathe, letting any perspiration escape to the outside of the material where it can evaporate away. A thermal top and a breathable jacket is all you need to wear for most winter conditions.

Safety wear

Being seen at night, particularly in poorly lit rural areas, is vital. Light colours will help but plenty of reflective material on all your shoes and clothing is essential. This is now standard on most winter jackets, training pants and shoes. If it isn't there, separate sticky reflective patches are available. Attach them to the areas that move the most, e.g. on your arms and legs, so that it is easier for vehicles to see them. Safety running bibs which sit over your training clothes are also a good idea.

An alternative to reflective patches is a small flashing light, designed for cyclists, but equally applicable to runners. It clips onto your shorts and the continual flashing can be picked up by a car at some distance.

Other equipment

Watches

Any runner intent on measuring improvement in their speed or endurance, needs a watch. Prices are now so reasonable that anyone can afford a model with all the basic functions plus a digital stopwatch accurate to 100th of a second and lap counting facility. If you plan to run marathons and want to take split times each mile you need at least a 26 lap memory. Control buttons on the front of the watch are easier to operate than those on the side. Optional extras, such as countdown times, metronomic pacers or even pulse or blood pressure readings are available at a cost.

Pulse meters

A pulse meter lets you train by your heart, rather than by time or distance. It is a more scientific way of training, setting the intensity of your training runs or sessions against how your body is feeling on any given day. Your mind might deceive you but your heart will not. In essence, it stops you over-training or under-training, by allowing you to train at the optimum level at all times. A basic heart monitor will give you a constant reading of your pulse, while more advanced models have alarms with pre-set limits which warn you if you are running too fast or too slow. The most advanced models can be down-loaded onto a computer.

It is a good idea to wear a stopwatch so that you can time your own performance accurately. In big races it may be several minutes before you reach the starting line.

Stretching

by Sandra Dyson

Most people accept that a 'warm-up' of some kind is always desirable before running without really understanding why it is necessary. Because of this, the usual procedure is to jog a couple of laps before getting started on the real training, or racing, and very often this leads to injury or at least a below-optimum performance. This chapter is mainly concerned with stretching exercises, where these fit into a proper warm-up procedure, and the benefits to be gained from this.

Basically, there are four elements in the warm-up procedure, which are as follows:
1 Light running.
2 Stretching.
3 Loosening.
4 Progressive speed increase.

Very few runners spend enough time on any of these elements. In the northern hemisphere, most training and racing seems to take place in cold, wet or windy conditions and thus it becomes even more important that you warm up thoroughly.

Light running

The initial light running is not simply an opportunity for a chat and to make sure that the lane markings go all the way round the track! It is the first step in

Long-term problems

Apart from the immediate dangers of injury or poor performance, there is the more insidious problem of a gradual loss of function because corrective action is not being taken during the warm-up.

bringing the body's internal temperature up to its best working level. Most scientific studies have indicated that there are many beneficial effects on performance from a proper warm-up. Perhaps the most important effect is the gradual increase that takes place in the coronary blood flow to the heart's myocardium, thus increasing the capacity of the body to perform work.

Also important are the changes that take place as the body temperature rises. With this increase in temperature there is also a corresponding increase in the speed of the metabolic processes within the cells, because those processes are temperature-dependant. For each degree of temperature rise, there is an increase in metabolic rate of around 12 per cent. This means that at these higher temperatures there is more rapid and complete separation of oxygen from haemoglobin and myoglobins, thereby improving the oxygen supply to the muscles during exercise.

The first step in achieving all these benefits, i.e. light running, needs to last for at least 15 minutes, varying with the weather, and only then is it time to move on to the next phase – stretching.

Stretching

What benefits can you expect to gain from always carrying out a thorough stretching routine?

Good flexibility will improve your ability to avoid injury by permitting a greater range of movement within a joint. If the joint is capable of a good range of movement, then its ligaments and other tissues are less likely to be strained since they can accommodate all but extreme positions. Certainly, tight-jointed athletes are more prone to muscle strains and tears than their more mobile colleagues, but fortunately the situation can be remedied since repetitive stretching of ligamentous tissue over a long period will give that increased range of movement. However, a word of warning: hyperflexibility must be avoided. Extremes of flexibility are of no value as the joint will then be weak at certain angles, making it prone to subluxations and dislocations.

In a recent study, injured runners, as part of their rehabilitation, were asked to wear inflated vests and run in water. It was found subsequently that there was a significant increase in range of movement. This resulted in an increased stride length, which road runners often find has shortened due to their high mileage.

The type of exercise used to achieve an increased range of movement is important. As a muscle is stretched, a muscle-protective mechanism is invoked, called the myotatic-reflex, which causes the muscle actively to resist stretch. Because of this, a vigorous, ballistic type of exercise will produce a contraction of the muscle – the very opposite of what is required. Hence the gradual and sustained stretch should be used by the runner.

So much for the long-term effects, but there are also more immediate benefits to be gained – for instance, the reduction of muscle stiffness and soreness. Muscle stiffness is a condition that most runners experience, particularly those involved in a daily running programme. When muscles are worked hard continuously, fluid collects within the muscle, causing swelling, shortening and thickening and it is a very slow process for these fluids to be absorbed into the blood stream. The process is speeded up, however, by gentle stretching, light exercise and mobilization.

More severe than commonplace stiffness is muscle soreness which can occur following a sudden change or an increase in the work load normally carried out. A fairly general soreness is likely to appear a few hours after exercise and this will last for about 24 hours. After this a more localized and specific soreness may be felt, which is called myositis, and usually lasts a few days before it wears off gradually. Until recently this soreness was believed to be due to minor tissue damage of the muscle fibre, or of the connective tissue. Recent research, however, suggests that at least in part the muscular soreness is due to tonic muscular spasm. Therefore, slow stretching of the affected muscles will help to reduce that soreness.

We have selected some exercises specifically designed to help build up a routine which can then be used throughout your athletic career. Use the exercises as a basis on which to build, for with a little bit of intelligent application, you should be able to work out for yourself which position you need to adopt to stretch a particular muscle group. All the exercises illustrated are of the slow-stretch type and you must not be tempted to 'bounce' into position, even if you see your colleagues doing so. Some of the exercises are more suited to an indoor area, some to a soft surface, but it is your responsibility to select one or two exercises from each group to give the balance required.

You will soon find yourself doing the exercises automatically as part of your warm-up routine. Even on days when you miss your training for whatever reason, it is a good idea to stretch and exercise your muscles. The exercises can be performed almost anywhere – in the gym, on the track, at home or even in the office.

Calf stretches

In the calf there are two major muscles – Gastrocnemius and Soleus. Gastrocnemius is the more prominent muscle, which has its origin above the knee. For this reason it can only be stretched by keeping the knee straight. The origin of Soleus, however, is below the knee and therefore has to be stretched with a bent knee. Of the five exercises illustrated, the first three are designed to stretch the Gastrocnemius muscle, and the other two, the Soleus, hence it is important that a selection from each group is included in the warm up.

1 Standing – raising toes
The exercises are graded in severity. This one is a gentle stretch which can be performed anywhere, at any time, but is nevertheless very useful, and a good prelude to the later exercises. Stand with the leg to be stretched about 30cm/12 inches in front of the supporting leg and draw up the toes of the forward foot as far as possible, leaving the heel resting on the ground. Hold for about 10 seconds.

3 Lunge position

Stand in a lunge position with the back foot facing forwards, unlike a true lunge, and the heel always maintaining contact with the ground. The front foot, which must be bent, should be as far forward as the rear leg allows. The trunk must remain erect as otherwise much of the stretch is lost. Hold for 20 seconds, continuously holding the stretch.

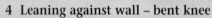

2 Standing – leaning against wall

Lean against a vertical support and about four feet away from it. Points to remember are that the seat must be tucked in and the heels firmly on the floor, with the feet facing forwards in front of you. As an alternative, and particularly if one leg is stiffer than the other, each leg can be stretched separately, the other leg being rested on the floor about 2 feet in front of the other. Hold for 10 seconds.

4 Leaning against wall – bent knee

Lean against a wall or similar object, as in the previous exercise, but this time 2 feet away from it. The hips must be tucked in again, heels on the floor, and the knees bent until stretch is felt in the back of the leg. Tightness may be felt anywhere along the length of the calf muscle, from immediately above the knee, down to the Achilles tendon. Stretch will vary according to the degree and type of exercise.

5 Standing – resting foot on object
Stand about 30cm/12 inches in front of a stool or similar object, approximately knee height. Place one foot flat on the object with the back of the heel to the back of the support. As the purpose is to stretch the bent leg, weight can be added with both hands. Because the knee is bent, this is another exercise which stretches the Soleus muscle. Hold for 10-15 seconds.

Quadriceps stretching

This is a group of four muscles which are situated on the front of the thigh. As one of these, Rectus femoris, has its origin on the hip bone, these exercises should be carried out with the hip extended (stretched).

1 Standing – holding foot
Stand, firmly holding one foot. The trunk must be kept upright, or much of the value of the exercise will be lost, and the leg pulled gently backwards. Hold this stretch for 20 seconds.

2 Kneeling on all-fours with one leg outstretched

Kneel squarely on all-fours with hands placed directly under shoulders, and knees under hips. Raise one leg backwards and allow the knee to bend so that stretch is put on the front of the thigh. Hold for 15 seconds and then repeat.

3 Kneeling – bent backwards

Start in an upright kneeling position, then, using the arms for support, lean as far backwards as is comfortable, making sure the knees are still on the floor. If your ankles are stiff, put a cushion under the feet. Hold for 10 seconds, increasing to 25 seconds.

Hamstring stretches

Of all the muscles, this group is the most neglected with regard to stretching, as shown by the number of injuries it suffers. The hamstrings are the muscles on the back of the thigh. They are biarticular, which means that they work over two joints, bending the knee and extending the hip. To stretch the muscles, the hip must be flexible and the knee straight.

1 Sitting – legs outstretched

Sometimes called 'the screamers', but not deservedly so! No exercise should cause pain, just a feeling of 'getting back to normal'. Remember that forward lean must start at the hips, and not just involve the spinal joints. The legs may be held together, but there are plenty of variations – legs apart, and stretching each leg separately, or bending one leg and stretching one leg at a time.

2 Standing – one leg resting on support

Stand about four feet away from a suitable support, and rest one leg on top of it. Keeping this leg straight, bend forwards from the waist and try to rest the head on the knee. Care must be taken not to reach first with the fingers, as this will only encourage the spine to bend at the top, instead of at waist level. As this exercise may well prove too difficult at first, start with the lead leg slightly bent. Hold 30 seconds.

3 Sitting – hurdle position

Sit with one leg outstretched and the other flat on the floor, with hip, knee and ankle bent to approximately 90 degrees. If this is not possible, the hip may be placed at a lesser stretch. Ensure that the back is bent from the waist, as the object is to get the head onto the knees. Some runners cannot even balance in the starting position, let alone try to lean forwards! If so, put a hand to the floor for support and practise until you can begin the proper exercise. Hold position for one minute, then change legs.

4 The plough

Lie on your back and take bent legs, together, over your head, supporting hips with your hands. The legs should be straightened at right-angles to the floor, and carried slowly backwards to touch the floor behind the head. Lie on a soft surface to protect the neck and spine. If you cannot manage this exercise with straight legs, try it with bent knees and, when comfortable, gently straighten the knees, with the feet still touching the floor. Hold for 10 seconds.

Hip muscle stretching

The range of movement of the hips during running reduces as the distance involved increases, i.e. the slower the running speed, the more restricted the movement. This tendency needs to be corrected and a selection from the following exercises will help to overcome this. It will be noticed that in all the following exercises, one knee is flexed. The reason for this is to reduce the pull on the hamstrings and so allow more movement at the hips.

1 Standing – knee to chest
Stand near to where there is some support, should it become necessary. Bend one knee fully and grasp it with both hands, pulling the thigh well into the chest to give maximum stretch at the hips. Hold for 15 seconds, then change over legs.

2 Ski stretch
Stand in a lunge position with back leg facing forwards and, bending front leg, gently lower body to floor until resting on hands. The back leg should be held straight and stretched as far back as possible. The heel should not be kept on the floor. Hold for 20 seconds, and then change legs.

3 Foot on support – knee flexed

Stand about 2 feet from a suitable surface. With one leg straight and supporting, place the other foot on the surface. This will give great stretch to the supporting leg. Hold for 15 seconds and then repeat the exercise with the other leg.

4 Side-stretching – leg on support

Stand at a distance from the support which allows the supporting leg to be at right angles to the leg on the surface. This exercise is often a difficult one for runners as it stretches the adductors, or inner thigh muscles. However, it is very effective and helps with the all-round balance required by the aspiring runner.

Trunk stretching

In running, there is very little movement of the trunk, the muscles working mainly as stabilizers. This encourages them to shorten and create stiffness, which may then adversely affect their running action.

1 Side stretch – arms above head

Stand with feet comfortably apart, hands loosely clasped. Raise arms above head and bend over to one side, reaching as far as possible. Hold the position for 30 seconds, but trying to lower the trunk very slowly during this time and relax the side muscles. Change sides slowly.

2 Rotation

Stand with feet about one foot apart and parallel with hands on hips. Slowly rotate the trunk to one side as far as it will possibly go. This is NOT a 'swinging' exercise. At the extreme of the rotation, hold the position for 20 seconds before returning to the starting position, then rotate to the other side for a further 20 seconds.

3 Lunge

Another lunge position, but this time the accent is on bending the back. Take a free-standing position, with both legs bent comfortably, and then bend backwards as far as possible, before holding the position for 20 seconds. For this exercise, there is no need to keep the heels on the floor.

4 Lying – back extension

Lie face downwards and rest one hand on top of the other. Holding the forehead against the hands, raise the whole of the trunk off the floor and then raise both legs as well. The object is to bend the back as much as possible. If you find it difficult to hold the position, try it first holding either legs *or* trunk, before putting the whole exercise together. Hold for 15 seconds.

Loosening

Having completed the stretching and flexibility work, it is time to carry out some loosening exercises. These are the dynamic type of exercises which take the joints through a wide range of movement rapidly. With the muscles, tendons and ligaments already stretched, this can be done safely and since one of the most effective methods of raising the internal temperature of a joint is to exercise it, this will quickly prepare the body for the last phase of the warm-up. The following mobilizing exercises can be carried out quite vigorously, and are a good lead-in to the final phase.

1 Ankle circling

Sit or stand and rotate each foot in both directions through a full range of movement. The exercise is performed better sitting, as then the ankle can be grasped just above the ankle bones, to prevent rotation at the knee. Although this is a simple exercise, it is useful in helping to eliminate the ankle 'locking' which many people experience at the beginning of a run.

2 Leg swinging

For this exercise, it is helpful, although not essential, to have some support in case of over-balancing. First, each leg is swung backwards and forwards, systematically increasing the height of the kick, and endeavouring to maintain a straight kicking leg, although the supporting leg may bend a little. Following this, turn to face the support and swing the leg across the body in both directions. Again, try to keep the swinging leg fairly straight, although the knee will not be locked. This leg swinging exercise is particularly good for stretching the hamstrings and the inner thigh muscles.

3 Arm circling

Stand with feet 30cm/12 inches apart and swing each arm in large, relaxed circles from the shoulder, allowing the trunk to follow the movement. Make sure that the arm is turned in both directions. It is a good idea to do this type of exercise in a circular or pendular movement.

4 Shoulder circling

This involves the shoulder girdle and not the shoulder joint. Standing with feet comfortably apart, let both arms hang loosely to the side of the body, then rotate the shoulders in a circular fashion. At first it is a good idea to practise the movements separately, i.e. shrug the shoulders and then let them gently down, and then roll them backwards and forwards. When these four aspects are accomplished, the shoulders can be rolled in a full, circular movement, but you should still keep the arms relaxed by the side.

5 Trunk circling

This can be done either with hands on hips or with outstretched arms. Again, stand with feet apart and then relax from the waist, making sure the back is fairly straight and not bending in the middle. From this position, start a large circle, going as far as possible into the range. A little practice will be needed to really benefit from this exercise.

Progressive speed increase

A series of runs can now be carried out, of up to 100 metres in length and gradually increasing in speed with each successive run, until running at full effort. By this means, over-loading of the muscle groups occurs, which prior to any power activity will give an increase in performance. It is thought that the increased load creates an increased excitation of the motor units of the muscles that have been called into play, and that this is then carried over into the actual performance.

All the benefits that have been gained through a conscientious warm-up will gradually wear off, so the closer the warm-up is to the performance, the more beneficial it will be. It is advisable to leave no more than 15 minutes between warming-up and the performance itself.

The challenge of the marathon

by Cliff Temple

In just a handful of years, the popular public image of the longest standard running event has changed dramatically. Even until the late 1970s, if you mentioned the marathon to most people they would admit it conjured up for them associations of exhausted men staggering through the closing miles, and in particular the famous film of the tragic collapse of Jim Peters within sight of the finish at the 1954 Empire and Commonwealth Games marathon in Vancouver.

Mention the marathon today, though, and the predominant image is of many thousands of people, of all shapes and sizes, happily jogging along in what for many of them has become simply a great community event. Yet the distance of 26 miles 385 yards (42.195km) is exactly the same. So what happened?

For a start, of course, there is a world of difference between an international athlete running for a gold medal in a major Games and the average man or woman aiming simply to complete the course. But even in big international competitions one rarely sees the leading runners in such severe physical difficulty as Peters these days; simply that of extreme fatigue after the race.

It is not due entirely to increased training loads either, because Peters himself was something of a revolutionary in the high quantity of his training, and also the zeal with which he tackled it. That uncompromising attitude may also have led to his undoing, because the 1954 Vancouver race was held in totally unsuitable weather conditions, with the temperatures on the unshaded course reaching the nineties. The combination of the appalling conditions in which the runners were asked to perform (only six finished), and Peters's refusal to modify his own flat-out habit of racing in the face of such conditions, led to the harrowing scenes of his ultimate collapse from heatstroke.

Today the more responsible organisers of many marathons try to ensure that their races are held in the best possible conditions for the runners (most marathons start early in the morning now to avoid the worst of the day's heat), and runners and coaches know far more about the demands of the event in so many important respects.

The other major development that has led to the booming popularity of the marathon is that it is no longer considered a race only for the elite. Indeed, it is scarcely a *race* for most participants, because the real challenge to them is not the other runners but their own ambition to complete the course successfully.

Thus the camaraderie now existing in the many 'mass' marathons that have sprung up practically everywhere is one of the prime features, as total strangers encourage each other through the difficult stages of the race, with no question of trying to beat each other, just a common will to share the experience of running the distance.

Its appeal is a mixture of many aspects to the first-time marathoner: the challenge, of course, of being able to run that far; the need for a dedicated preparation period, with a near certainty that if you can complete the preparation then you should be able to complete the distance too; and the subsequent improvement in fitness, tone and health that is a by-product,

Eamonn Martin raises his hands in victory as he wins the 1993 London Marathon. The marathon has become one of the most popular mass running events of our time for runners of all abilities.

even for those who do not quite complete the course.

Above all, though, it is the doors that have opened in the running world itself which have contributed to the marathon boom. Now races actually cater for the vast number of runners who, just a few years back, would have found that the officials had packed up and gone home when they finished.

At the 1993 Nutrasweet London Marathon, 5,993 of the 24,450 finishers bettered 3½ hours – a much smaller proportion of the field – with the last recorded finishers taking over eight hours. But they got round. The total number of marathons in the UK in 1978 was just 17. By 1980 it had risen to 33, and then shot up within the next couple of years to more than 130! Now that total is much less, as the 10km and half-marathon events have expanded in number, but the world over city marathons continued to attract thousands of runners. The marathon had changed beyond recognition.

But what of the race itself? When did it start, and what does it represent? The first marathons were held in 1896, when the Olympic Games were revived in Athens. As a tribute to a legendary Greek messenger named Pheidippides (who was supposed to have run from the village of Marathon some 24 miles to Athens in 409BC bearing the news of the victory by the Athenians over the invading Persians, before collapsing dead from his exertion), it was agreed to stage an endurance event at the 1896 Games over the route supposedly

taken by him. The event was won, appropriately, by a Greek, Spyros Louis, and was the only Greek victory of those Games. However, the event caught the public imagination, and it became a regular part of the Olympic programme.

Training for a marathon

The one inescapable fact to be faced by everyone preparing for a marathon is that it is a Very Long Way. So what it needs primarily in racing terms is basically running, running and more running. Diet and shoes can be refined to some extent to help the runner to a small degree, but you cannot eat your way to fitness, nor can the best shoes in the world run the race for you.

So for the beginner hoping to run a marathon, the first stage is to decide when, either roughly or exactly, you want to tackle the big event, and then work

The standard distance

At the 1908 Olympics, staged in London, the marathon was run from the private grounds of Windsor Castle (so that the royal children could see the start) to the finish at White City Stadium, West London. The distance of that race, 26 miles 385 yards, was adopted in 1924 as the official marathon distance, but until that happened marathon courses often varied considerably in length.

backwards from that date in establishing your own preparation. If you are an absolute beginner to running then you should allow at least six months of build-up to the event. It has been done in less, but I would not recommend it, as not only will the training itself be less substantial but the risk of injury is that much greater through trying to hurry progression.

For those in their late thirties or older, a preliminary check with your doctor is strongly advisable to ensure that he knows of no medical grounds that would prevent you from undertaking the training. In most cases, the doctor will probably be delighted to hear of your increased exercise plans, as long as you intend to graduate them moderately.

If you have not taken much physical exercise for some time, then you should spend a preliminary week of walking for 30-40 minutes a day at a comfortable pace, to re-introduce your body to the internal processes of exercise.

Then gradually introduce running, by alternately walking and running for 100 metre stretches for as long as you feel comfortable. All running should be at a slow, conversational pace, because if you are puffing and panting, then you are going too fast. Slow down until you reach the stage where you can talk and run at the same time. Don't worry if it feels as slow as the walk at first; it will improve, as your cardiovascular system gradually adapts to transporting more blood (and with it oxygen) around the body.

If you continue this for several weeks, you will notice a strengthening of the legs, an improvement in your breathing, and that you can run for longer periods without walking. The eventual aim, of course, is to cut out the walking intervals altogether, and just run continuously for 10-15 minutes and more at a time. There is no hard and fast rule for how many training sessions this should take. Instead, be guided by your own body. Above all, the regularity of this training is of the utmost importance. Over-doing the training one day and then taking three days off to recover will not help you progress.

The event is 99 per cent aerobic, which is to say that oxygen is supplied to the muscles at the same rate at which it is used, as opposed to, say, an 800 metres track runner, who has to run so fast that his body simply cannot keep up and gets into oxygen debt which is only repaid by the enforced gasping for air after the race.

Sure enough, the world's top marathon runners may cover each mile in under five minutes, whereas a lot of us would be unable to run even one mile flat out in under five minutes. But these runners are so fit that to run at a pace of a mile every five minutes is their equivalent of our seven minute mile pace, or 10 minute mile, or 12 minute mile; it takes no more out of them.

So let us do away with any idea that running marathons involves running fast all the way, while gasping for breath. What it does involve is running for a long period at a steady pace, and it is your ability to continue this process for 26 miles, your stamina, which is being tested. Therefore the need in training is to gradually develop the capacity to run further and further. However, as you get fitter so the distances with which you can cope become greater. So, to some extent, does the accompanying fatigue.

Adding variety

When you can run four to five miles every day you should start to add more variance to the training programme by continuing to increase the distance run on every other day (say, to seven miles), but on the intermediate days remain at four, or less.

The reason for this is that the body needs time for recovery and regeneration as part of nature's process of strengthening. As you train more and more, so the need for some degree of rest becomes as important as training itself, and many international runners are not afraid to take one day completely off running each week. Nor should you be, as long as you are satisfied that you are fulfiling an adequately progressive training programme on the other days.

Several months after the start of your training programme, the development of mileage per day might go something like this over a four-week period:

Day 1	Day 2	Day 3	Day 4	Day 5	Day 6	Day 7
5	5	5	5	5	5	5
7	4	5	5	6	4	3
8	4	6	4	7	4	Rest
9	4	7	4	8	5	Rest

Instead of miles, which are not always easy to calculate, you may prefer to work in terms of 'running minutes', i.e. total number of minutes spent running each day. But, either way, dropping down on alternate 'easy' days between the harder, progressive days not only gives you a physical but a mental break, as indeed does that rest day at the end of the week, which runners often jealously guard.

The next stage, then, is to choose one day of the week on which you could considerably lengthen your training run with a view to eventually approaching the marathon distance itself.

Most people choose Sunday morning as the time for their long run, leaving them the rest of the day to relax or recover, but any day suitable to your own routine will do. The idea is that this one run will be the session of the week in which your body adapts to running for anything up to two or three hours.

Building up fitness

Then, as you become fitter, the momentum carries you along. It is probably harder to actually build up from 30 seconds of jogging to five minutes, than it is to go from one hour to two hours. For once your cardiovascular system is working well again, then it is simply a question of building up stamina.

Once a week is sufficient for this long run, but you should start to think about introducing a semi-long run – say, two-thirds of the distance of the long run – at a mid-point to the week. This may involve changing the pattern of the week around again, so that you might end up with: 15 miles – 5 miles – 7 miles – 10 miles – 5 miles – 8 miles – rest.

As you run more and more, so you become fitter almost without noticing it. Your pace increases with no apparent extra effort, as you are simply becoming more and more efficient in your running. Without turning every training run into a time trial, it is worth keeping a record of

It is inadvisable to train too much on the roads; hard surfaces can eventually cause injuries. Try to vary your training between road and cross country running. Here marathon runner Sally Eastall trains on her local country lanes.

your time for a particular course as a means of checking progress. But be fair, and do not continually try to beat your record, or you may over-reach yourself. Just run at a comfortable pace and do not look at your watch until you have finished. You will be surprised how, over the weeks and months, the times come down without any effort, other than that of getting out and running regularly.

Running surfaces

According to the season of the year, you may be limited in the surfaces on which it is possible to run. In winter, for example, most people have to do their midweek

running after dark, and usually on the road. Apart from the potential risk with traffic (always wear light coloured training kit to help the motorists see you), continual pounding on the roads places a tremendous strain on the legs. On every stride the unremitting concrete sends shock waves of several times the bodyweight up through the legs and the back before being totally absorbed.

Too much running on this type of surface can lead to shin soreness and eventually stress fractures in the foot or lower leg, which are common injuries among long distance runners. Thus it is advisable whenever possible to run on grassland or cinder paths where the shock is considerably less. On the other hand, a certain amount of road running has to be undertaken to adapt the legs to the shock in preparation for the race itself. So ideally the runner should use both surfaces, alternately if possible, but neither to excess.

Shoes and running action

Shoes, of course, can play an important part in reducing and absorbing the shock, and considerable attention should be paid in their selection. Look for shoes that are comfortable all round and do not pinch or squeeze the toes. Some models come in different width fittings, but all should have considerable support under and around the heel.

Most long-distance runners land heel-first and then roll on to the forefoot. Good protection is needed here too and do not be tempted to buy lightweight shoes. The lighter shoes are made primarily for top-class runners who tend to be both light in weight and light on their feet. If you are neither, and if you expect to be running slower than 2½ hours for the marathon, then the extra weight in a more substantial pair of shoes will be more than compensated for by the added protection and shock absorption the heavier shoes will give you.

Before the actual marathon, wear the chosen shoes on a few long runs to make sure there are no inner seams or other irritants that could cause blisters.

Preparation and clothing

Before a long run or marathon race, grease around your toes, arches, the heels, the armpits, crotch and even nipples. You could tape the nipples for protection.

Every item of clothing that you intend to wear in the marathon itself, even underwear, should be worn at least once in a long training run beforehand to ensure that under 'battle conditions' there is no unsuspected problem with it, such as an irritating vest-seam, or shorts which you find you will have to hold up with one hand if it rains.

In general, the clothing should be loose and airy, and light coloured, particularly if the weather is hot; white is a particularly good reflector of the sun's rays, whereas dark colours tend to absorb them. Of the weather conditions you are likely to encounter, heat is the marathon runner's greatest enemy because, while you can put on extra layers in the cold, enjoy the refreshing qualities of rain, or shelter from the wind, you cannot escape from heat.

Dehydration

Continuous physical exercise in itself produces heat in the body, but when the air temperature is already high, then trying to lose that heat build-up becomes a major problem. Sweating is the prime method, but in excess this in turn can lead to dehydration, and the taking of drinks before and during the race on a hot day is very important to replace the large quantities of fluid lost through sweating.

Convection, the cooling of the skin by a slight headwind, also helps, whereas the use of a wet sponge to cool down the face, neck, shoulders and thighs is an artificial method permitted by the rules. Sponging stations are situated about every three

miles in most marathon races, while in between these are the drinks stations.

It is certainly worth getting used to taking a drink on the run before the race itself, because to run and drink at the same time is an art of co-ordination in the extreme. It is easier when the cup is only half full, and it is often preferable to control the contents by placing your hand over the top of the cup or pinching it until you have steadied it before starting to drink the liquid.

Diet and nutrition

Most first-time marathoners go into the race with an uneasy feeling about 'hitting the wall'. This expression refers to the point that usually occurs between 18-22 miles, when the body's supply of glycogen, the energy source stored in the muscles, has been used up, and while the body switches to fat for its fuel, the runner suddenly feels drained and may slow dramatically, even by several minutes a mile.

The feeling comes on so suddenly and without warning that it is literally as though you have indeed run into a wall. The bounce goes from the legs, and in extremes you may be turned from a reasonably fluent runner at 22 miles to an aspiring survivor by 23. Some runners say they never hit the wall, particularly top-class performers who may simply have trained their bodies to such a fine degree that the change-over from glycogen to fat happens so fluently that they just do not notice it.

Avoiding heatstroke

On a cool or cold day, drinking during the event becomes less important, but on a hot day it is essential, as the spiralling stages of dehydration could lead to heat-stroke. So a few mouthfuls before, and whenever possible during, the race will help prevent disaster. After the race take in plenty of liquids (but not too quickly) until a normal pattern of urination gradually returns.

Carbohydrate-loading diets

In the late 1960s, one of Britain's greatest ever marathon runners, Ron Hill, developed a form of carbohydrate loading diet (originally used by long-distance cyclists in Sweden) in an attempt to artificially increase the amount of glycogen stored in his muscles, and thus delay the moment of hitting the wall.

The original technique involved what is called a 'bleed-out run', in which the runner covers some 20 miles at a good pace seven days before the race to deliberately deplete his supply of glycogen. For the next two and a half days he takes very few carbohydrates in his diet, concentrating instead on high protein and fat, while continuing to train lightly. From lunchtime on the third day, he switches to a high-carbohydrate diet while continuing to eat proteins, minerals, vitamins and fats and still training lightly.

The idea behind the diet is to fool the body into producing extra glycogen-storing enzymes during the period of near abstinence, so that when the diet switches to the carbohydrates section, more can be stored. However, this diet does have some disadvantages. For a start, during the initial stages of the week, many runners feel tired, lethargic and jaded, and may be prone to catch any virus which is going the rounds. Their resistance is lowered. Another setback is that stored glycogen needs between three and four times its own weight of water, so that by the end of the week the runner may feel bloated, and will

There are drinks stations on most marathon routes and you should take in plenty of liquid in hot weather to avoid dehydration.

not have trained hard for six days. Even if he has not succumbed to any germ, he will still need a lot of will-power to feel that he is going to run well in the forthcoming race. For it is not until 18 miles or so that the benefits of all that pre-race suffering come into play, and in some cases runners have reported no apparent benefit, or even dropped out before reaching that stage.

What suits one runner may not suit another. The diet still has its ardent followers, although Hill himself has moderated his original scheme, taking a little more carbohydrate earlier in the week. There is also a theory that if it is used too often, the body 'catches on' to what is happening, and the system will then not work properly. Also the drastically revised food intake, compared to normal, may lead to digestion problems, particularly as the training simultaneously is reduced considerably. Some runners now adopt only the second half of the routine – the enjoyable part! – and even then take care to increase only the *percentage* of carbohydrates in their diet rather than the actual volume.

The best advice for first-timers is to avoid tampering with your diet, and concentrate on getting everything else right. Remember, too, that it was developed by a runner who was already one of the world's best and was looking for

methods that would give him that vital half per cent advantage over his rivals, having already reached saturation point in his training mileage.

Final preparation

How do you prepare for the Big Day? The easing down period for a marathon – the gradual descent of that aeroplane for landing, if you like – really begins about a fortnight before the race itself. At that time you have reached, hopefully, your highest week's training mileage, and your longest individual training run.

Let us suppose that the previous week you have totalled 60 miles. The total for the penultimate week before the race should be about two-thirds of that, so in this case it would be 40 miles. In the week immediately before the marathon, around 20 miles would be enough.

So, with a clear conscience, you can cut back on training as the race gets closer. You may find, ironically that you may even feel tired and heavy on less training, whereas you might have expected (and this does happen too among some runners) to feel more energetic than of late.

If you do feel heavy and tired, there is no need to panic. Very often when you approach an event for which you have long been preparing you find that the body seems to have switched off subconsciously in preparation and is preserving itself for the main event. It seems to know, however much you may

---

Running tip

What you eat on the day of the race depends very much on the starting time. If it is an early morning start, like 9.30 or 10am, then you will need to be up early anyway. Something light, like toast or cereal, will give your stomach food to work on without causing indigestion, but eat at least 2½ - 3 hours before the start.

Marathon checklist

- Running shoes
- Clean socks
- Running vest
- Shorts
- Tracksuit or sweatshirt and spare bottoms
- Nylon rain suit (if necessary)
- Marathon number
- Safety pin
- Plasters
- Petroleum jelly/vaseline
- Tissues
- Hat and gloves (if cold)
- Spare shoe-laces
- Race maps and instructions
- Large plastic bag for kit
- Headband

try to fool it into thinking otherwise, that these last training runs are not the Real Thing. Do not worry because when the gun goes off in the race itself, all is well again.

In the last two days before the race, you should do virtually no running at all. You may want to have a short, gentle run on the day before the marathon, possibly just enough to make a final check on all equipment, while your last major meal should be on the night before the race; otherwise you may experience digestive problems.

Race day

Before leaving home for the race, check that you have everything you need, including (if the organisers have posted it to you) your number. At some marathons you have to queue to collect your number before the start, and this could waste not only time, but also nervous energy.

Prior to the race stay as relaxed as possible. Work through your own pre-race routine, performing some stretching exercises, visiting the toilets, smearing on petroleum jelly, and sipping some liquids if it is going to be hot. The amount of pre-race jogging you should do is minimal.

In major races, the competitors usually line up in groups for the start according to their best, or anticipated, times, with the fastest at the front so that the slower runners do not get trampled in the stampede. Wearing a digital wristwatch can be a great help, not only to keep an eye on the time before the start, but also to record your own time during the race itself and at the finish.

In a field of some thousands it may take five minutes or more to even cross the starting line for the runners at the back, yet the official times recorded will still take your time from the moment the gun fired. So if you start your own watch as you cross the line you will have a far more accurate idea of your total time for the 26 miles 385 yards.

The biggest trap into which you can fall is to be carried away in the excitement and start off at a pace that is much too fast for you. Alternatively, trying to match strides with someone who is going just a little too fast for you is also a mistake.

Every single runner will have a different background of ability, training, experience and ambition, and only much

Many runners include some hill training as part of their marathon preparation. Some top athletes even wear a special weighted jacket to help increase strength and endurance as shown here.

later in the race are you likely to find yourself running with someone of a similar overall standard to yourself. Until then you will be passing people, being passed, and then re-passing the same people, as everyone tries to find their own individual comfortable pace.

If, for example, you have trouble holding a seven minute miling pace for 10 miles in training, then it is less than likely that on race day you will be able to hold six minutes miling for 26 miles. So if you find yourself going through five miles in 30 minutes, then ease right back because you are over-reaching yourself at this stage,

and there is a long way to go. Most people can expect to run a slower second half to a marathon, unless there is a lot of downhill running in the closing miles.

Eventually comes the moment for which you have trained, as you cross the finishing line, not forgetting to stop your digital watch, as the clock over the line will not have taken account of your delayed start. Some people run dozens and dozens of marathons in their lifetime but still say nothing compares with finishing their first one.

Breaking three hours

Once you have conquered the distance, then the path to improving your time will take in two other considerations: speedwork and exercise. Not that you should abandon your established sessions of steady running, nor the one very long run during the week. If anything, they become an even more essential part of your training if you want to head towards, and under, three hours. But now that you have laid the foundation with your background of steady-paced training, you can afford to move on.

If running faster in the marathon involves taking a slightly longer stride, then the speedwork you should undertake to further improve the cardiovascular system (which you have so far developed purely and patiently by steady running) will involve a considerably greater stride.

So the first step, so to speak, is to gradually increase the range of movement of the hamstrings and tendons by exercises, so that you can minimize the risk of injury which is present when you do try to run significantly faster.

Simple exercises, such as standing with your feet crossed over, then bending forwards towards the ground so that you feel the hamstrings stretch at the back of your thighs, can help. So can placing the heel of each foot alternately to waist height on a table or chair, holding each there for 10 seconds in turn, and continuing for several minutes.

The term 'speedwork', of course, is relative to the event. For an 800 metre runner, speedwork may mean repetition 400 metre runs in 52 seconds. Yet for even a world-class marathon runner, the same distance run in only 67 seconds could be deemed speedwork. However, he would probably run far more repetitions in a session than the 800 metre runner, reflecting the contrasting natures of the two events.

What speedwork (in the sense of running faster than racing pace for a given distance) does for the marathoner is to push the pulse to a higher level than it would reach in straightforward steady running. In turn, that can dramatically improve the ability of the circulatory system to shift blood around the body quickly. But it is no use trying to do that until you have established a lower level of efficiency, i.e. through steady running.

The other point is that marathon speedwork is not necessarily run 'flat out'. If, for example, you are running 400 metre

intervals in an average of only 90 seconds, then you are still running six-minute miling pace, or approximately 2 hrs 38 mins pace for the whole distance. So twelve or fifteen of those runs, with a two minute recovery jog in between, would certainly have some benefit for the runner aiming to better three hours.

The side effects of such speedwork on your steady sessions should be noticeable too, as you should find it possible to run them even faster with no more effort. Eventually you will need to be covering some of your shorter steady runs at close to six-minute miling pace, because breaking three hours for the marathon requires an average of 6 mins 50 secs per mile. So if you only ever train at seven to eight-minute miling, you could not expect to be able to churn out 26 consecutive sub-seven minute miles in the race.

Gradually, the components of the ideal week come together: the long, steady run of 20 miles or so, which can be at seven to

> ● **To stretch the Achilles tendons**
> Stand facing inwards on a step or kerb, with your heels two to three inches over the edge. Then gently lower your heels together, half an inch at first, then three-quarters of an inch or further, so that you are gradually increasing the stretch, but without strain. Repeat this 15 times in all. In due course, both hamstrings and tendons will regain their full range of movement.

eight-minute miling; then the bulk of steady mileage during the rest of the week, at least half of which should be at six-and-a-half minute miling pace or faster if you are having a serious shot at breaking three hours in the marathon; and then the speedwork, once a week, with sessions like 12 or 15 x 400m in an average of 90 secs, with two minutes' rest in between, *or* 20 x 200m in 40-42 secs with a 200m jog in between, *or* even 6 x 800m in 3 mins 15 secs, with five minutes' recovery. Do your stretching exercises every day.

A final consideration is hills. The traditional hill session of running hard up them, and then jogging back down, is probably of less value to the marathoner than incorporating some stiff climbs into the steady sessions, and then practising the art of running in a relaxed fashion up and over the top, without breaking your rhythm. The pace in the marathon, remember, has to be continuous and economic.

24-week training schedule

This special 24-week training schedule will help you build up gradually to your aim of breaking three hours on marathon day. In this way you can develop speed and strength for a better time as well as endurance to stay the course.

WEEK	WEEKLY MILEAGE	SUN	MON	TUES	WED	THUR	FRI	SAT
1	40	10	6	4	8	5	Rest	7
2	45	11	7 fartlek	5	8	7	Rest	7
3	50	12	8	5 fast	9	6	Rest	RACE 10
4	55	12	8	6 fast	9	8	Rest	2 x 6
5	60	12	8	8 fast	9	8	5	RACE 10
6	60	14	8	6 fast	10	2X6	Rest	10
7	65	14	2X5	8 fast	10	2X6	Rest	11
8	55	15	8	6 fast	10	6	Rest	RACE 10
9	65	15	2x5	8 fast	12	8	Rest	12
10	70	16	2x5	10 incl. hills	12	10 fartlek or interval session	Rest	12
11	65	16	2x5	10 incl. hills	12	1 hour fartlek or interval session	Rest	RACE 10
12	75	17	2x5	10 incl. hills	12	2x6	Rest	8x6
13	65	17	8	10 incl. hills	12	1 hour fartlek or interval session	Rest	RACE 10-12
14	80	18	8	10 incl. hills	14	1 hour fartlek or interval session	2x5	12
15	70	18	2x5	10 incl. hills	12	1 hour fartlek or interval session	Rest	RACE 10-13
16	85	20	2x5	10 incl. hills	14	1 hour fartlek or interval session	9	8-6
17	80	20	2x6	10 incl. hills	14	1 hour fartlek or interval session	6	10
18	75	18	2x5	10 incl. hills	12	1 hour fartlek or interval session	4	RACE 12-15
19	90	12	2x6	10 incl. hills	15	1 hour fartlek or interval session	7-4	22
20	60	10-8	5	8 incl. hills	12	1 hour fartlek or interval session	4-5	Rest
21	70	RACE 20	8	10 incl. hills	14	1 hour fartlek or interval session	2x5	Rest
22	80	22-24	5	10 incl. hills	14	1 hour fartlek or interval session	2x5	10
23	50-60	15	5	8 incl. hills	10	6	Rest	6
24	50	10	Rest	6 incl. hills	6	Rest	2 jog	THE RACE

Chapter 5

Veterans
running begins at forty

by Sylvester Stein

During the past decade, veteran running (or masters, as it is known in the USA) has become one of the fastest growing, most flourishing sports movements in the world. It has taken its place at the leading edge of the amazing running boom. Since the marathon era started at the beginning of the 1980s, hundreds and thousands of men and women have dedicated themselves to the challenge of the long, long run, and even larger numbers have taken up other aspects of running.

The veteran section in particular has been gaining ground relatively to the other age groups lately, if only for the fact that the early younger recruits have become distinctly venerable by now, and yet have not dropped out. Meanwhile, the new intake straight into the 'vets' has continued, in two separate streams: at the base, the ageing and hardened, very competitive club-runner, now too old for the first league; and for sheer quantity the amateur New Breed men and women joining the big boom with the motivation of getting themselves into shape as middle age approaches.

By definition these fun runners are already in their thirties and forties and thus well qualified to become official veterans, the joining age being 35 for women and 40 for men. Many do not join the movement and take up running and racing until their fifties, sixties and even seventies.

In the United States, the 'masters' running epidemic spread fast. Now it is happening in a big way in other countries too. The major road marathons and races are paying more and more attention to the vets – and rightly so, as vets number one-third of their competing armies. Athletics clubs are putting on extra track meetings for vets and the specialized vets clubs themselves are flourishing.

In the first years of the boom the existing national organisations did not look too encouragingly at the vets. The novices had their inferiority complexes, and the old breed often found their noses put out of joint – a runner who may have been dominating his group for a decade or so would suddenly be beaten at the tape by an upstart. It did not make for the happiest of relationships even in a sport that lacks the arrogance of so many others! However, today both types have found respect for each other and are fully merged into the

You can be as competitive as you like – running in fun runs, track events or, as shown above, in road races. Vets events are well supported, standards are high and competition is fierce.

immense and comprehensive vets' running network that has been set up over the years.

There is a wealth of choice for the older runner: competition is divided into five-year age groups, so that here too there is a winning chance for everyone. After all, where is the forty nine-year-old who would pit himself against the new recruit of forty, bearing in mind that a top forty-year old marathoner, say, is still capable of racing against the best in the country of any age?

On the track the same situation holds. Ex-internationals compete shoulder to shoulder with men and women who simply decided one day in their late thirties and forties that they would like to have a go. There is the case of Rob Bush of Highgate Harriers in the UK who took up running eighteen months before his fortieth birthday to concentrate on the 400m on the track. He trained assiduously, waiting to strike, and just after he turned forty, he won the British vets indoor 400m championship against all comers in the excellent time of 52.8. There are even people *entering* track events in their sixties and seventies.

Whatever type of running you are in, and for whatever reason – sport, health, fun, social – you should join a vets club. There you will find the best advice on training, health and injury, the best information on up-and-coming races, the fellowship, the competition and the social milieu. Even those who prefer to be solitary runners should join a club.

Good health

Of all the reasons for running, surely none can be more compelling than the fact that although exercise does not put years on your life, it can put life in your years! For centuries there has been a widespread belief that adequate vigorous physical exercise is necessary to preserve life and its desirable qualities into old age. Discussions of this thesis have intensified in recent times but there have been many scoffers who asked: 'Where is the formal evidence?'

Medical science would not enthusiastically support the exercise and running movement without having this evidence.

Gradually, during this past decade, firm evidence began to accumulate, until in 1984 the British Sports Council's Fitness and Health Advisory Group were able to call for a 'move forward' and back the exercise lobby, even to state that the over-forties need only seek medical advice to take up running 'if there is a relevant medical history or symptoms'.

Finally, in 1986, a major scientific study was published by one of the world's leading experts on running and health, R.S. Paffenbarger. This was a huge statistical survey of Harvard 'alumni' stretching back over forty years and

showed that if he took regular exercise in the years since leaving college the average 'alumnus', by now almost a veteran, would earn two or three years' extra span of life.

It was, of course, specifically running that most of these Harvard people took up. Thus it clearly demonstrates that running protects and enhances life. For running does the job of keeping you youthful and fit and it is the best counter to the malaises of the middle-aged: reluctance to exercise (which leads to heart disease); overeating (ditto); and cigarette smoking (leading to heart and lung disease and many other problems).

Running tackles all these almost automatically. Starting in reverse order, it is well established that runners seem no longer to want to smoke once they start to train. In a survey conducted by *Running Magazine* in the UK (now *Runner's World*) it was discovered that only three per cent of readers smoked. An American running magazine survey revealed that only one per cent of their readership smoked, although forty two per cent had done so previously.

As far as overeating is concerned, how can you stuff yourself when you have a training run or race in three or four hours' time? So you moderate your intake, and after your run, you never feel as hungry anyway.

With the matter of people's reluctance to exercise, running works its magic in a

Many elite athletes continue running and racing as vets. Here the British athlete Dave Moorcroft takes part in a vets road race.

way that has not been given sufficient credit. It is the only practical way in which an individual can actually *keep* to a programme, unlike all those other diet and exercise routines, which are started and dropped after a week. Runners keep going.

Time and tide

Once in the movement, all kinds of runners, even the strictly non-competitive, are keen to measure their times against the best. The first thing one of the New Breed is sure to ask is: "How close am I to the world record?" The answer to the beginner is that it takes years to get yourself into the best possible condition. You must have patience. If it has taken you ten or fifteen years to degenerate into your present non-active state do not expect to be rewarded with total fitness after ten or fifteen days.

This piece of bad news contains by implication some very good news: you can expect to go on improving steadily during your first three or four years in the sport even against the tide of the ageing process. As the heart and muscles learn from your regular training sessions they get stronger, you yourself get race-wise from experience and gradually your act comes together. Then it becomes possible for you to look with hope, not only envy, at the performances of the great and the famous.

Slowing up slowly

As a new veteran gets into running he or she will improve for three or four years as stated above. Thereafter the runner will slow up gradually. All of us slow up with age. As the bones, muscles, reflexes, lungs and heart lose some of the quality, speed drops away. What can you expect your own rate of slow-down to be? For most vets it is a matter of about one per cent a year; and it is surprising how that round figure is mostly very near the mark.

Below are two graphs, plotted from world age group tables of the 1980s, which show the statistical decline in performance by age of top competitors. Each individual exhibits a very similar picture. One slight

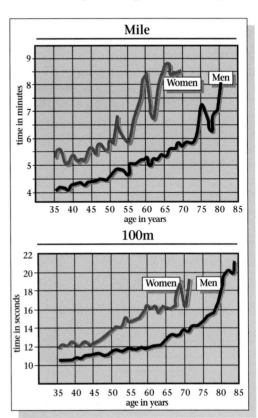

exception is that the decline in performance by age is somewhat slower the longer the race – perhaps this is because pace judgement and mental stamina count for more in the longer races than in the sprints, and age does not erode those qualities – the very opposite, in fact.

Development plan

The beginner with ambition needs an introductory course of action to follow. Here is some simple and general starting advice. Once you are well into these opening weeks you will inevitably come across more detailed information.

1 Take it easy in your first weeks
Make a point of not overdoing it, because it is so easy to get too enthusiastic and land up with an injury. We do not want you to do that, because that way we might lose you – you could throw overboard all your motivation by being out of things for several weeks while the injury is healing. How do you avoid overdoing things? Here is a simple rule: make up your mind before a run just what you are going to do and do not exceed this, even if you are feeling wonderful – wonderful is what you are supposed to feel *after* a good run! Also, decide at the beginning of the week on your mileage, and stick to your target.

2 Wherever possible, run on grass until your legs and feet get toughened up. Do not worry if your shoes get dirty or your toes wet – keep away from too much pounding of roads and tracks.

3 Enjoy yourself Go out only as often as you feel like it. On the other hand, remember that once you are warmed-up you *do* feel like it; one minute into a run is always enough to throw off that tired feeling, so get out of your easy chair anyway.

4 And, for emphasis, another reminder: join a club as early as you can.

Training

Whatever your aim, whether it is to emulate the stars or to aim at soft standards, you will be wanting to improve; and to do that you will need to train hard.

The majority of veteran runners follow distance-running training programmes. Training patterns are much the same as the younger athlete's in terms of mileage, but different in speed-work and tempo-running where the veteran seems to do less. There are notable exceptions, of course, but in general the veteran distance runner will regard a fast 3km or a brisk 8km as adequate pace work in his training programme. It is noticeable that many experienced veterans who still enjoy competing do not have the appetite for repetition pace work and interval training that they once enjoyed.

Charles Smart, a noted British runner in the 1940s, continued his speed training well past his sixtieth year. "I cannot understand," said Charles, "why, as runners slow down with age, they do less speedwork rather than more." Smart recognised that after many years of training, veterans build up a reservoir of stamina through their careers and are probably better equipped to face endurance events than their younger counterparts. And yet these veterans invariably accentuate the trend by doing more steady mileage and less speed.

A noted British veteran who has not fallen into this trap is Laurie O'Hare who commenced running in his late twenties and although he won representative vests for Southern Counties AAA and Middlesex he never reached international status. Yet, when he became a veteran, O'Hare was running life-time bests, winning world veteran track titles, and finally took the world age-best 3,000 metres track time

Be wise with speed

Nearly 300 years ago Edward Young wrote: "Be wise with speed; a fool at forty is a fool indeed." Young was not speaking of running, of course, but his words are relevant on both counts. The young athlete can acquire speed very rapidly after the endurance phase. His suppleness and speed of adaptation may soon lead to his running flat out without any ill effects. However, the older athlete must proceed with more caution. He is less supple and takes longer to adapt. He must have a very high respect for the injury risk in speedwork and feed it to his body in carefully rationed doses. So, be wise with speed.

from the great Olympian Alain Mimoun.

O'Hare (now over sixty years old) still follows the speed training patterns he was using twenty years ago, and his last-lap kick still has plenty of sting in it. Laurie joins up his short speedwork to his long-distance running with 2 x 2 mile sessions on the stopwatch. "I have a good warm-up running out to a nice flat two miles stretch of grass and do a few preliminary strides. I then run the outward stretch at a fast tempo on the watch, jog for ten minutes and then zip the homeward run, in similar time."

Most of the veterans who take part in track competition follow the same training principle as the younger athletes: speed is built up on a winter's diet of endurance training, fartlek and cross-country racing.

Training schedules

Little has been written about training schedules for veterans and their wide range of age-groups, which is perhaps a good thing. It is unwise for a young athlete to follow a schedule slavishly, particularly when it has not been tailor-made for him. It would be doubly unwise for a veteran to do so. Far better to study the principles of training and, by experiment, to find out what is best for you. Training is the art of combining all the ingredients previously mentioned, in the right proportion for a particular individual. Arthur Lydiard, the famous New Zealand coach, constantly stressed that the athlete at peak form must be equipped with every armament from a

50-metre sprint to marathon endurance and must be able to produce anything between those distances without warning during a race. To do so, you must practise running all distances up to the event of your choice at racing pace.

The principle is the same for all ages but the veteran would be well advised to follow the advice of Bill Bowerman, the United States track coach, who advocates alternative hard/easy sessions for his young athletes. Intensive speed sessions are broken up by steady running to give the body a chance to adapt, besides giving the mind a rest, too. In the case of older runners, it would be prudent to keep their speed sessions even further apart, say, every third day.

Some veterans have taken it for granted that they can pick up schedules from their youth, step up the mileage, and then battle their way through to glory. However, most come unstuck, and the ones most likely to succeed are those who are not in too much of a hurry to follow a modestly graded schedule. Indeed, some successful veterans have followed Lydiard training schedules but doubled their length by using them only on alternate days, with a steady run on the in-between days.

When plenty of steady endurance work has been assimilated, and tempo runs and some speedwork have been added in the right proportions for you, then you will eventually experience the joys of running at your true optimum pace. It will be most satisfying to realise that all the grit, determination, patience and skill that went into your training programme have produced the desired result. But do not be greedy. When an athlete is at his peak it requires more willpower not to train than to over-train. There have been many notable examples of international athletes reaching world-record levels in their racing preparations and squandering their newly-won resources before the big day because they did not have the courage to ease off.

Runners are notorious for believing that rest means loss of form, but 'rest' is a relative term and does not mean putting your feet up! Veterans must also learn to recognise the danger signals of over-training or over-racing. If you think you feel the warning signs, then introduce a few days of easy running. You will lose nothing by this. You should always err on the cautious side.

Stretching

No training or racing programme will be valid without a regular stretching schedule. There is not a single runner who can get away with dodging the stretching work on the muscles. Here are some stretching disciplines developed especially for veteran runners, drawn up by Brian Webster who works as a Chartered Physiotherapist, is a member of the Midland Vets and a physio to the Great Britain athletics team. Brian has planned these notes for runners whose 'mobility is diminishing with advancing years'.

Stretching exercises are the 'in thing' of the 1980s and 90s, just as LSD was

during the 70s and circuit and weight training before that date. Therein lies the danger: because everyone agrees that stretching exercises are a good thing, a lot of people spend far too long stretching with little or no benefit. But veterans need not feel guilty, as some of them obviously do not spend *long enough* stretching. There are three good reasons for stretching:

1 To reach your existing limit of mobility.
2 To regain your mobility after injury.
3 To increase your mobility if you are too stiff.

Reaching your limit You need to reach your limit of mobility first thing every morning and before training or competition. A simple, safe way to do this is as follows: move slowly to what appears to be your limit. Give four or five gentle, rhythmical stretching movements getting a

It is particularly important that you always stretch before training or racing. This will aid flexibility and help prevent injuries and stiffness. Make stretching an integral part of your warm-up routine.

little further each time (but do not 'bounce'). It does not take very long.

After injury Regaining mobility after injury is very important. When a muscle or ligament is injured we tend to hold the limb in the position of ease – we never put it on full stretch. Healing takes place but we may end up with a slight limitation of movement. Stretching can start on the second or third day after injury. Move slowly to the comfortable limit and stay there for a few seconds. If it gets easier move a bit further and stay there. Each stretch should be sustained for 10 to 20 seconds and repeated about six times. The aim should be to regain full stretch in two to three weeks and the rule is 'no fast running until you have got full pain-free stretch'.

Too stiff?

Increasing mobility is hard and takes time. The question is: "How much mobility do you need?" Running a marathon requires no more mobility than walking, whereas sprinting requires considerable mobility. As many vets are middle-distance runners and as most of these do some speed work, we will look at their mobility. There are three muscles that get injured due to lack of mobility: hamstrings, calf and quadriceps. Three quick tests will tell you if you have enough mobility here.

● Hamstring test

Hamstrings are stretched when you bend down to touch your toes. If you can nearly touch your toes with feet together and knees straight, then you are OK. If you can only get halfway down your shins, you need to stretch.

● Calf muscle test

Stand with arms in front of you, fingertips out-stretched and just touching a wall. Keeping heels on floor, bend your elbows. If you can touch the wall, your calf muscles are OK.

● Quads test

Standing, bend your foot towards your buttocks. Does your heel touch your buttocks? Now try the other leg. If your heels reach your buttocks then that's fine.

Good Morning routine

1 Arms stretch overhead with fingers linked
2 Side bends, sliding fingers down side of leg to knee level
3 Trunk rotations
4 Full knees bend
5 Bend forward to touch toes

That only takes about one minute! Before training or racing add:

6 Calf stretching – stand three feet away from a wall. Place hands on wall and incline forwards by bending elbows, keep heels down and knees straight
7 Quadriceps stretch – bend foot up behind you. Grasp ankle and pull heel towards buttocks

That only takes two minutes, but it is also very important to start each training session or warm-up with slow running and to speed up only gradually.

If you cannot even catch hold of your ankles – then you have got work to do.

If you are limited in these tests, then work at it. Move slowly to the existing limit and maintain the stretch for up to 30 seconds. Repeat six times. do not expect quick results. Increasing mobility is a long slow job. Always try to exercise with stretching *and* strengthening (for instance, circuit training).

Women's running

The latest growth area in running has been for women. Because women are eligible to be vets at thirty five years of age this new trend is also effectively a veteran trend. All the veteran clubs accept women members at the same level as men, and competition is provided for women wherever it is required.

This is only natural, in spite of the fact that it has taken some years to come about. It has been harder to get the women started, in spite of the fact that the benefits of running for women are even greater than for men – in improving their shape, their enjoyment of life, their physical and mental confidence and, most especially, their health. However, the women's bandwagon has finally got rolling.

The international and world scene

In the United Kingdom, the British Veterans Athletic Federation is the institution that represents vets nationally. At the same time, it is one of the associations of national bodies that make up the World Association of Veteran Athletes (WAVA) and as such authorizes the individual vet in this country to become part of a team.

Anyone who is a vet may opt to compete internationally. There are no standards and no selection processes. On the other hand, there is no organisation that will pay for your trip abroad. It is part holiday and part competition.

International veteran running is certainly a great opportunity for travel. World veteran championships are staged every two years and in the alternate years there are European championships.

Whatever your standard you are accepted as part of the scene. The championships include not only the full track and field programme but also a 10km cross-country event, a road walk and a marathon.

Other smaller parties regularly attend the Italian Veteran Championships and events such as the popular Bruges 25km in Belgium. All of these events represent the icing on the cake; you do not have to be at your very best to compete, but it is more satisfying if you are really fit. As each occasion approaches, a little more spice is added to your training sessions.

So, whether you wish to run just for fun, for fitness or to explore your competitive potential you will always enjoy the benefits of running, whatever your age. For the veteran runner, age is merely a state of mind; birthdays are merely stepping-stones to the next class. There are no limits, no restrictions, as you can start running at any age.

Women runners

by Cliff Temple

The rapid progress made by women runners in recent years would have amazed even the early pioneers of the 1920s, who fought so long and hard to establish athletics as a sport suitable for women as well as men, often in the face of hostile reaction.

However, at the end of the nineteenth century, the idea of women taking part in taxing physical exercise was still alien to society, although a Greek girl named Melpomene gatecrashed the first Olympic marathon in Athens in 1896, and was alleged to have completed the course in around 4½ hours. In 1918 a French woman, Marie-Louise Ledru, finished thirty eighth in a men's marathon (time unknown), while in 1926 Violet Piercey ran the famous Windsor to Chiswick marathon course in 3:40:22. But these are isolated incidents, probably recorded at the time more for their novelty value than as a serious indication of the growth of women's distance running. That was to take nearly half a century longer.

Some areas of women's athletics were being taken a little more seriously by the 1920s. The first international governing body for women's athletics, the Fédération Sportive Féminine Internationale, was founded in Paris in October 1921, with six original members, including Britain and the USA. However, a request for women's events to be included in the 1924 Olympic Games was turned down by the International Olympic Committee. In response, the FSFI staged its own 'Women's Olympics' in Paris in 1922, later known as the World Games, and subsequently held every four years until 1934, by which time nineteen nations were taking part.

In the meantime, the IOC relented and allowed a representative selection of five women's events in the 1928 Olympic Games. Unfortunately, women distance runners were almost out of the Olympics as soon as they were in, because in the longest race in Amsterdam, the 800 metres, several under trained women collapsed just before or after the finish of the race (won by the German Lina Radke in 2:16.8). Subsequently, Olympic officials decided that women were too delicate to run such long distances and so no race over 200 metres was held again until 1960.

It is only in the relatively recent past that women's endurance events have been included in the Games programme. The 1500m was first introduced in 1972, and the 3000m and marathon in 1984, although ironically the winning time of American Joan Benoit in that inaugural women's marathon in Los Angeles would have won any of the men's Olympic marathon titles up to 1948. In 1988 the

The American runner Joan Benoit was the first winner of the women's marathon, staged for the first time in the 1984 Los Angeles Games.

head in the mid 1960s. In 1966, a Canadian, Roberta Gibb, joined in the famous Boston Marathon in the USA and completed the course, untroubled and unofficially, in 3 hours 20 minutes. The following year an American, Kathrine Switzer, managed to obtain an official race number by signing her entry form 'K. Switzer' and starting the race in a big, baggy tracksuit, alongside her boyfriend.

In an incident that subsequently passed into running folklore, a Boston official realised that Kathrine was actually female at around the 18 miles point, and tried to physically push her off the course. Her boyfriend in turn man-handled the official, and the incident was graphically recorded in the press the following day. Kathrine finished the course, but was later suspended by the American Amateur Athletic Union for her deliberate deception. She later became a heroine to hundreds of frustrated women runners around the world who wanted to be allowed to run long-distance races, but who were restricted to events no longer than three or four miles at that time.

By the early 1970s, the marathon was at last recognised as an event for women in the USA, and races like the Boston and New York Marathons introduced women's categories into what had previously been male-only preserves.

An international sports promotion campaign by Avon Cosmetics included lobbying international and Olympic officials around the world to include the women's marathon in the Olympics, and

women's 10,000m was added to the Olympic programme too, with Britain's Liz McColgan taking the silver medal.

The determination of women runners to prove that they could indeed run further and faster than many male officials believed them capable really came to a

Ingrid Kristiansen, seen here winning the 1985 London Marathon, is still the record holder for the women's marathon. She was at the forefront of the revolution in women's running in the 1980s, and her example helped to inspire many women to run.

helped smooth the path of the subsequent inclusion of women's marathon events in the European championships (from 1982), World championships (from 1983) and Olympic Games (1984). Yet, just a few years earlier, some sports medical experts had been doubting whether the female body was capable of running 26 miles, let alone at the sort of pace which soon became common among the leading competitors.

The first sub-three hour marathon by a woman came in 1971, yet it took only eight years for the record to dip below 2½ hours, in 1979, and then continued a rapid advance towards the first sub-2 hours 20 minutes clocking. Grete Waitz, the elegant Norwegian runner, had set a world best of 2:32:30 on her debut in the New York Marathon in 1978, then proceeded to hack the record down in chunks to 2:25:29 by 1983. Joan Benoit (2:22:43, also in 1983) and another Norwegian, Ingrid Kristiansen (2:21:06 in 1985, still the current record at time of writing), took it even further.

The running revolution

But although these performances completely revised what physiologists had thought was possible for the female runner, the women's running revolution was by no means confined to the upper echelons. The real story was in the many thousands of women of all ages who took to the roads for a whole variety of reasons, few of these connected with trying to win races. The changing social attitudes not only made it acceptable for a woman to

in 1980, Avon staged an alternative 'Olympic women's marathon' in London the day after the end of the Moscow Olympic Games. A field of over 200 women runners drawn from 27 countries set off from Battersea Park, and created history. It was won by New Zealander Lorraine Moller in 2:35:11. It was races like this, and an earlier international women's marathon staged in Waldniel, West Germany, by the German doctor and coach, the late Ernst van Aaken, which

You are never too old nor too young to enjoy running. It can be fun to run with your family: on holiday, in the local park at weekends or even in organised fun runs.

admit a fondness for exercise, but positively desirable.

The increase in opportunities to take part in local fun runs with the family, and even road races where the accent was on gentle participation, meant that more and more women were encouraged and motivated to jog or run regularly.

Targets were set. Completing a fun run, or even a marathon, became the reason for getting out of doors, even when it was raining. Mothers and grandmothers,

teenagers and those who couldn't remember when they had last used their feet, all found in this new approach to running an aspect they had perhaps missed during their schooldays: that the pleasure can come from your personal improvement, even if that means breaking 10 minutes for the mile, or an hour for 10 kilometres.

Physiological differences

One controversial set of predictions was made in the early 1980s by Dr Kenneth Dyer, senior lecturer in social biology at Adelaide University, who published suggestions based on his statistical researches that over the shortest distance, the 100m sprint, women might actually catch up with the men by the year 2054.

And at longer endurance events, such as the marathon, he suggested, it might happen as soon as 1990. We know now, of course, that it didn't. The world women's marathon record remained in 1993 to the credit of Ingrid Kristiansen, as it had done since 1985, even though a huge impact was made on other middle distance records in 1993 by the Chinese women. But were the Chinese simply taking the events along a path of natural progression rather than posing a serious threat to 'catching' the men?

Wang Junxia, just 20 years old, led the charge and at one point in September 1993 herself bettered no less than four world records in six days during the Chinese National Games in Beijing: the 10,000m, the 3000m (twice) and the 1500m, even though she finished second in the shortest distance to another world record-breaking Chinese, Qu Yunxia.

But at her longer events, Wang Junxia, the 1993 world 10,000m champion, reduced the percentage gap between the men's and women's world records, which had long hovered around an 11.5 per cent differential, to just 9.5 per cent in the 10,000m with 29:31:78, and an even more surprising 8.3 per cent in the 3000m with 8:06:11.

Yet in making such progress, the Chinese women had brought to the sport a new level of determined training, which often included running the equivalent of a full marathon a day at high altitude. The reports of their training indicated they were attempting volumes previously unattained by women, and somehow managing to remain injury-free. The impact the Chinese made at the 1993 World Championships in Stuttgart, where they swept the track titles from 1500m to 10,000m, had already indicated that new levels of performance remained untapped. Shortly afterwards, in their record-breaking spree, they proved it.

Wang Junxia set new world records in 1993 at 3000m and 10,000m. Here she is shown running (number 316) in the leading group of athletes in the 1993 World Marathon Cup in San Sebastian.

There was, perhaps inevitably, widespread talk of drug use at the time, but it was emphatically denied by the Chinese and their hard-driving coach Ma Junren, and certainly all their tests proved negative. What they had achieved, after many years spent by China in the athletics wilderness, perhaps had more to do with generations of hard-toiling workers to whom the discomfort of distance-running training must have seemed comparatively easy. Even though a considerable number of respected observers of the distance running scene remain convinced that the Chinese performances were achieved genuinely, they also remain unconvinced about Dyer's predictions that the women will eventually catch up with the men.

For Dyer's prophecy had been based on a 'catch-up' pattern traceable through statistics which would inevitably be coloured in part by the fact that women have participated only in organised athletics events much more recently than men. As their levels of training increased, and experience was gained, so standards rose.

The development of more refined training techniques, with scientific monitoring processes, and better shoes, nutritional advice and racing programmes, helped both male and female performers to improve. If the women's 10,000m world record was broken in 1993, so was the men's, twice in little more than a week. So while the women may appear to be closing the gap, the men's events are still apparently some way from complete development.

However, once aspects like competitive frequency and event experience have been progressed to their fullest extent, the major limiting factor to further reduction is physiological. And it is here that the disadvantage women have when compared to men seems likely to prevent equality of performance from ever becoming a realistic prospect.

Three major areas in which women suffer disadvantages are in:
● Their lower muscle mass.
● The lower oxygen-carrying capacity of their blood.
● The considerably greater percentage of body fat.

Men have around 5-6 litres of blood in their bodies, compared with 4-4½ litres in the average woman, and in men a higher percentage (47 per cent) of that blood comprises red cells than in women (42 per cent). The oxygen-carrying capacity of those red cells is measured in terms of haemoglobin per unit volume of blood, and even here the mean value for men is around 15.8g/100ml and for women only 13.9g/100ml.

These figures mean that during a steady run, women need to transport a total of nine litres of blood around the body to deliver one litre of oxygen whereas men need only eight litres of blood for the same amount. Women also have smaller hearts relative to their body size, and smaller lung volumes, making it even harder to contemplate performance equality.

The higher percentage of body fat in the female, which may still be around 15

per cent in a highly trained woman endurance athlete, compared with as little as six per cent for the equivalent male, is far less than in the average woman, however. A healthy untrained man would probably have a body fat percentage around 12-15 per cent, whereas in a woman a figure of 25 per cent would not be unusual.

Where the additional fat deposits are a burden is in events below the marathon, where they are equivalent in some respects of 'dead weight'. However, in the marathon and beyond, these fat deposits can provide fuel for energy, giving the female a positive advantage over the male.

Any woman can run, no matter what her age. It is best to start off gently and gradually; if you are competitive, you may enjoy taking part in a fun run.

Maximizing potential

However, the men still run faster, even at 100km, and to concentrate too much on the possibility of women catching up men is to detract from the more relevant aspect of how women can best take advantage of their growing opportunities in running. Regardless of whether or not they equal male performances, how they can best maximize their obvious potential?

It would probably be true to say that the majority of women who take up jogging (which is really just slow running) and develop into more ambitious runners do so initially to lose weight and become trimmer. While diets can work to some degree, the actual process of burning up calories through exercise can accelerate the weight-losing process. But it does take time, partly because first you need to become sufficiently fit to run far enough to have any noticeable effect on your weight.

So if you have just started gentle jogging for 10 minutes a day, you must expect initially to experience some stiffness in the legs and no immediate weight loss. Don't lose heart, because the stiffness indicates that some 'training' effect has taken place in your legs, and if you keep up the routine regularly the stiffness will vanish and you will feel stronger and able to jog further and faster but with no

Safety

Many women runners prefer training in pairs or small groups, not only from the social side, but also for the regrettable need in some areas for greater security. Fortunately, there are relatively few incidents but even one is one too many, and it would be unwise not to be aware of the potential threat that may exist, however slight.

Firstly, unless you definitely prefer to run alone, try to make arrangements to meet up with a training partner if you are venturing into lonely areas. If you prefer to run alone, or circumstances dictate that you must, then take commonsense precautions of ensuring someone else knows where you are running and when you expect to be back.

Some women run with a hatpin, or a loud whistle, concealed on them as a defensive weapon if they are anxious about the area through which they are going to run. There is no need to feel you

are being unduly alarmist in doing this, any more than if you take out insurance on your house. You don't expect anything to happen to it, but if it does, you want to be prepared anyway. One habit that is best to break, because it might actually invite trouble if you run alone, is to follow the same time on the same day every week. Varying your routes and your time of training is the best common sense safeguard.

more effort; probably less, in fact.

After the first week or two, in which you may wonder if it really is doing you good, you will also enter one of the most exhilarating phases of your training as you realise it *is* doing you good. You find that, through the regularity of the exercise, you are coping noticeably better, as your body remembers how it used to run with no effort when you were a girl. Turning the clock back (or at least halting its forward march!) is always a morale-booster in itself, and fairly soon you may well find that you are hooked on running.

The side-effects of a run help to sustain you, as you realise you can get into your own mental world at least once in the busy day. The feeling of well-being that running creates has been labelled 'Runner's High', and is attributed by physiologists to the release of hormones known as endorphins in the brain, triggered off by the exercise itself. The burning-up of calories, the release of bottled-up tension created by the day, the oxygenation of the blood, the use of the heart and lungs, and indeed the operation of the whole body in taking the simple exercise for which it was designed so long ago, combine to give you a physical and mental boost.

Another side-effect is that you feel less inclined to nibble between meals. Running actually dulls the appetite for some time afterwards, but because you are feeling trimmer, fitter and happier with yourself, you are less likely to keep looking in the cupboard for comfort foods.

Other problems

Some women runners become alarmed when their periods disappear for no apparent reason and they know they are not pregnant. In fact, they are almost certainly experiencing amenorrhoea, a condition that is still not fully understood but which occurs in response to stress, severe dieting or, most usually in the runner's case, hard training. It may be the fatigue levels, or the drop in body fat associated with hard training, that cause the onset of amenorrhoea. It is a common condition among endurance sportswomen, particularly distance runners, and also among those women whose involvement in activities such as gymnastics, ballet or modelling, keeps them determined to maintain a severe degree of slimness.

One theory is that the body stops ovulation if the fat stores drop below 15 per cent as a reaction to the possibility that there is famine in the land and that therefore the woman should not start another life if it cannot be sustained.

Certainly, amenorrhoea is also an early symptom of the so-called slimmer's disease, anorexia nervosa, which is actually a psychological illness experienced mainly by adolescent girls who develop a deep fear of becoming fat, and reject food to a severe degree. With a mortality rate as high as 10 per cent, the onset of anorexia has to be recognised early by a sufferer or their family or close friends, and expert help sought.

Differentiating between a serious distance runner with amenorrhoea as a result of her hard training and an anorexic who may dabble, even seriously, in distance running as an additional form of reducing her weight, is often difficult. Anorexics are sometimes drawn towards an activity like distance running because it is an area where slimness is admired and encouraged. Some of our leading distance runners admit to anorexic tendencies, which is not the same as suffering from anorexia itself. However, there are runners who see successful athletes like Zola Budd and Mary Decker-Slaney, all extremely thin, and believe that to be successful themselves they have to be skinny. In each case, though, Budd and Decker were always, and will always be, very thin. For different body types to be forced to emulate that degree of slimness can lead to a number of side-effects which will actually have the opposite effect to that desired.

Anaemia

A lack of strength, an inability to repair damaged muscle tissues, or even to properly support the normal life systems, can affect the underweight athlete. An additional hazard is the possibility of iron deficiency anaemia, which can be brought about by the pursuit of slimness through an incomplete nutritional intake, or simply through iron loss in the blood during menstruation. A short course of ferrous sulphate tablets taken with meals can quickly correct this problem, which

Zola Pieterse (formerly Zola Budd) is a naturally thin athlete. Here she is seen running in the 1993 Great North Run in the UK.

otherwise can seriously reduce the ability of the blood to circulate oxygen around the body. In any athlete, male or female, the possibility of iron deficiency should be investigated if there is an inexplicable loss of form. Although many leading women runners experience no periods during long bouts of hard training, a reduction of the load either through injury or when easing down for a major competition quickly brings about the return of menstruation, with no apparent adverse effects on fertility being noted. But one recently-reported side-effect of long spells of amenorrhoea may be an increase in the incidence of stress fractures among hard-training athletes. Scientists have observed that the cessation of periods also induces a deficiency in the hormone oestrogen, which plays its part in bone formation. Thus with weaker bones, and a continuing heavy training load, runners who have had amenorrhoea for a substantial time seem more susceptible to stress fractures. Now scientists are working on a special pill which would restore oestrogen levels artificially.

Pregnancy

If a runner becomes pregnant, unless there are any medical indications to the contrary, it is usually quite safe to continue training within the guidelines of their own comfort. As the lump gets bigger, so the pace will of necessity drop, and some doctors insist that the pregnant runners in their care should never run fast enough to get into oxygen debt, because they are then, they explain, depriving the foetus of oxygen as well as themselves.

Inevitably, there are occasions when an athlete, although pregnant, still competes, blissfully unaware. Ingrid Kristiansen competed in the 1983 World Cross-Country championships, and only when

Many women continue running well into their pregnancy. However, although it is usually safe to continue with gentle training, you should consult your doctor if you plan to do this, especially in the later months of your pregnancy.

disappointed with her thirty fifth place and seeking medical explanation did she find out that she had raced while four months pregnant – but she still delivered

a fine, healthy baby. In general, women with a background in running tend to have easier deliveries than non-sporting mothers.

In fact, they may even be better runners afterwards. One American declared with feeling that "Compared to having a baby, running a marathon is easy!", while in the Soviet Union research by leading physiologist Professor Vladimir Kuznetsov

Ingrid Kristiansen (centre) was four months pregnant when she competed in the 1983 World Cross-Country Championships.

indicated that 'the birth of a first child seems to strengthen the organism physiologically and gives some form of reserve of energy, perhaps in preparation for a second birth. Psychologically, it seems that women are more prepared to train hard after giving birth.'

Training for the club athlete

by Harry Wilson

Whether you are aiming to be the best in the world, the best in your club or the best in your road, the same principles will govern your training. The range of events covered by this chapter, i.e. 800m to 10km, is quite wide, so obviously there will be certain differences in the training followed. These are mainly related to the physiological requirements of the events and the physical qualities possessed by individual athletes.

Some of these distances are predominantly aerobic events, i.e. the oxygen utilized by the athlete whilst running is roughly sufficient to meet his energy requirements, and there is little build-up of lactic acid. However, in other events, there is a large amount of anaerobic activity (oxygen uptake is insufficient to meet the runner's energy requirements) involved, especially in the following circumstances:

1 An inexperienced athlete who has not yet developed a high oxygen uptake and consequently moves into the anaerobic energy process sooner than more experienced runners. In this instance, he should include more aerobic training in his programme until he has improved his oxygen uptake.

2 In shorter distance events where the speed level is much higher.

If your main aim as a distance runner is going to be improving your oxygen uptake, then it is vital that you are physiologically suited to do this. Each person's muscular system consists of a mixture of slow twitch and fast twitch fibres. A heavy predominance of slow twitch fibres means that you will be more suited to endurance activities, whereas a predominance of fast twitch fibres implies that you will do better in explosive activities. It is no coincidence that a muscle biopsy carried out on Alberto Salazar, the former marathon world record holder, revealed a make-up of approximately 95 per cent slow twitch fibres, and it follows that great middle-distance runners such as Steve Ovett and Seb Coe would probably have something closer to a 50:50 ratio of both types of fibres. So if you are naturally blessed with a high proportion of slow twitch fibres then it follows that endurance training can bring about major improvements in your

73

running but if you have the other type of fibres, the amount of improvement that can be effected by such training is limited.

It is not necessary to carry out a muscle biopsy to determine your muscle make-up. If you can do an endurance activity such as running or cycling for a reasonable length of time, say a minimum of 30 minutes without undue distress, then it is probable that you possess sufficient slow twitch fibres to bring about a good improvement with intelligent training. If you can also sprint short distances (60-100m) quite well or can produce a fierce acceleration, then it points to you having a good proportion of fast-twitch fibres and you could also benefit from anaerobic training. Other physical attributes that will help are:

1 A strong healthy heart acting as a powerful pump to circulate the oxygen-carrying blood to and from the muscles, and to carry away the waste products of exercise.

2 Large lungs inhaling large quantities of air and a good chest expansion allowing the lungs to expand as they take in air.

3 A reasonably proportioned frame; obviously the ideal is someone who has long legs attached to a short, light and powerful torso, but many people have done well in endurance events without possessing this ideal physique.

Of course, you cannot choose the heart and lungs with which you are born, but intelligent training can make healthy organs more efficient. The heart is a muscle, and, like any other muscle, it will become more powerful with exercise. The inter-costal muscles, which control chest expansion, are also strengthened and made more effective by regular activity.

Running technique

It is important to develop an efficient and economical running technique early on in your running career, as it is extremely difficult to change a running action which has been 'grooved-in' as a result of thousands of miles of running. Your style of running is related to your physical attributes. Your technique is affected by the proportion and dimensions of your limbs, by your muscular strengths and weaknesses, and by your degree of suppleness. However, any idiosyncracies of style should not alter the fact that there is a mechanically correct way to run and you should always try to be as efficient as possible. An inefficient stride is multiplied approximately 800 times for each mile run, so you can see how much difference this can make on long runs.

The basis of the runner's action is to place one leg in front of the other and for the arms to work in time with the legs, i.e. left arm forward with right leg and vice-versa. You do not need to learn this technique as it is natural to all of us. Each runner modifies this basic action to produce an individual style but you should be satisfied that your own style is both efficient and economical.

Developing strength and endurance

You can try out these exercises to help develop strength and endurance. All you need are two ordinary telephone directories or heavy books. Do 20 repetitions of each exercise once a day to develop chest, back and shoulder muscles. The exercises will not necessarily make you put on weight.

Stand with feet shoulder width apart and raise each arm alternately.

Hold the telephone directories by your side, then raise them slowly and smoothly to shoulder height while keeping your arms straight.

Start by holding the directories out-stretched to the side at shoulder height, then swing your arms forward and back keeping the movement controlled and level throughout.

Hill running exercises

● Running up a gently sloping hill, about 400m/500m long. Run with a normal action and resist the temptation to shorten your stride to make the exercise easier. Your knees should be pointing forwards and always keep in the back of your mind the thought that you are not running these hills to achieve fast times but to develop a sound technique.
● Fast running up a steeper hill of about 80m/100m in length. Run with an exaggerated thigh lift, placing the emphasis on maintaining the action throughout the length of the runs.a steeper hill of about 80m/100m in length.

Run with an exaggerated thigh lift, placing the emphasis on maintaining the action throughout the length of the runs.

Leg action

Most runners naturally develop a suitable leg action and stride length without having to be taught. We have an instinctive way of adapting stride length and foot placement to suit varying circumstances and surfaces, and it is rarely necessary to tell a runner how to vary his technique according to the speed required. As you get fitter and stronger changes happen automatically in the length and power of your stride. You have only to stop running for a while and put on a little weight to see how quickly your stride shortens when you start running again. The important things to look for in your leg action are as follows:

1 That your knees point straight ahead.

Any turning inwards or outwards of the knees will result in your feet being planted similarly out of alignment. This means that instead of all the drive being in a forwards direction, a certain amount of effort is wasted in a sideways direction. Turned-out knees are often a sign of insufficient strength in the thighs, which can also seriously affect you if you attempt to sprint, or when you tackle hills on the road or cross-country. I recommend hill running for strengthening thighs.

2 Make sure that you use your feet correctly to assist leg drive. In distance events, you usually make contact first with your heels and then roll forwards to drive off the front part of your feet. To gain more speed, you probably move even

further forwards so that when you sprint, the final part of the drive is from the toes. The 'flat-footed' runner lands heavily on his heels, fails to achieve any 'foot-roll', and is unable to use his feet as another lever to assist leg drive. This fault is usually due to weak calves or lack of mobility in the ankle joints and the fault cannot be overcome simply just by asking the runner to use his feet correctly. Strength and mobility must be there to enable the feet to assist the legs, and I suggest that this type of runner does rotating-type exercises to achieve greater ankle mobility, and heel-raising exercises for calf strength. Running over soft, uneven ground will also develop mobility in the ankle joints, whereas uphill runs will strengthen the calf muscles.

Remember that if you have strong and resilient legs, you are equipped to run on all surfaces and will rarely suffer from the injury problems that beset the runners who are weak and inflexible.

Arm action

In distance events, a good running technique means an economical use of energy, but we often see energy being wasted by unnecessary arm movements. You need a relaxed, swinging type of arm action to counter-balance the easy striding action necessary for distance events. It is only when you use violent and powerful leg movements for sprinting that you need to use similar arm movements.

For any movement of your legs there is an equal and opposite reaction by the upper part of your body, and you must ensure that your arm action gives an economic reaction. If your arms are not used properly, then your shoulders will provide the reaction, and shoulder movements are both wasteful and slow (the shoulders and upper part of the body will twist, and it should be noted that much more energy is needed to move these large masses than is needed to swing the lighter arms).

Arms should be flexed at roughly 90 degrees and should swing easily backwards and forwards slightly across the front of your body. Easy paddling movements of the forearms will have no ill effects, but always keep your elbows low and close to your body. If they come too far away from the sides, then your body and shoulders will develop a wasteful, rolling action.

For the major part of a distance race, you should carry your arms low, but I advocate a more powerful action during fast surges or the finishing burst. Then, the arms should be raised, flexed more and used with speed and urgency through a large range in an attempt to make the legs work with the power of a sprinter. During the final burst, speed, not economy, is the decisive factor, and it is particularly important to be able to make a quick change into this sprinting action.

Most long distance runners are usually adequately equipped to use their arms correctly for the major part of the race, but some runners are not sufficiently developed in the upper body to be able to quickly adopt a powerful finishing action.

Emile Puttemans *(white vest) and* **Lasse Viren** *(dark vest), were both world class runners at distances from 3000m to marathon.*

1 *and* **2** *These two pictures show the finish of the 'driving phase'. the left leg extends powerfully as full use is made of the foot as a lever and the right thigh swings up prior to extending to gain stride length. High knee-lift gives extra stride length as the foreleg automatically swings forwards at the end of the knee-lift. Leg strength and mobility in the hip, knee and ankle joints play an important role at this stage and it appears that these factors rather limit Viren's action. Leg strength enables the runner to apply great force against the ground and mobility in the joints allows him to extend the drive well behind the body and gain thigh lift.*

3, 4 *and* **5** *The drive has been completed and the runners are now in the ground-covering 'recovering phase'. The left leg begins to flex naturally as a result of the powerful extension. In this and the next phase ('support') we can clearly see the relaxed action of two skilled runners. There are no unnecessary movements of head or arms as such movements use up precious energy. A runner must be well conditioned to run in this relaxed way, but if he has any energy-wasting actions that affect his running, then constant attention to these details will eventually result in his running naturally in an economic way. Both Puttemans and Viren show an efficient, compact arm action and there is no sign of tension in the neck, shoulder or hands.*

6 *The left leg has swung back and the right foot is coming lightly to the ground with the heel making contact first. The middle distance runner makes no attempt to reach out and pull back with the feet as this would be far to tiring.*

7 *As the body-weight begins to pass over the right foot, the left leg folds up into a short lever. Flexibility and strength of drive determine whether or not there is a high back-lift. There is a marked difference at this stage in the two runners and the difference can be traced back to the amount of drive shown in pictures 2 and 3. It is difficult to say which is the more correct action as in the longer distance events stride length must always be related to*

economy of action, i.e. Viren may not cover so much ground as Puttermans with each stride but his action may use up less energy.

8 *The whole of the right foot is now in contact with the ground in the midle of the 'supporting phase'. The only function of the right leg at this stage is to support the body-weight and the calf muscle gains a moment's relaxation. The legs are 'resting' and so are the arms.*

9 *The body-weight has now moved over and in front of the right foot at the beginning of another 'driving phase'. Note that the feet point straight to the front so that no drive is wasted in a sideways direction.*

Improving oxygen uptake

A great amount of a long-distance runner's training will be done aerobically, and it is this type of running that brings about the greatest improvement in the athlete's ability to take up oxygen in the lungs and then dissociate it to the muscles. With aerobic training, you will raise your heart rate soon after the start of running and maintain this rate at a fairly even level throughout the session. This effect is usually achieved by long steady-state runs and varied-pace sessions, provided that the fluctuations in pace are not to marked and do not bring about violent changes in the heart rate.

Remember that during even-paced long runs there will be some variations in your heart rate as you encounter uphill stretches or when you increase your pace on downhill sections. Change in terrain can also affect heart rate, as it obviously requires more effort to run over heavy plough than on flat, even grassland. This steady or near steady-state running has the effect of moving huge quantities of blood around the circulatory system, and research has shown that this form of exercise produces greater capillarization, i.e. opening up more channels for blood to be carried to and from the working muscles.

The pace of the steady-state runs will depend on the length of the run and your level of fitness. However, I like to think that you should train over a range of distances and paces, varying from the short fast runs (3-4 miles) to the long easy run

Your training threshold

You can determine your own training threshold (i.e. the intensity of exercise needed to bring about any training effect) by the following method:
1 Count your heart rate at rest in beats per minute
2 Get someone else to count your maximum heart rate in beats per minute, e.g. immediately after a flat-out effort over 300/400 metres
3 You now know your present pulse range; add two thirds of this to your resting rate and you have a rough guide to your training threshold. As long as you are exercising at a rate either above the result figure or not more than 10 beats below the figure, then you will experience some training effect from the exercise.

(15-20 miles). The length of the training run will be related to your racing distance and thus 1500m runners would not include so many long easy runs as those athletes who are going to race over 10km. As the speed of the runs determines the level of pulse rate, it is quite likely that a 10,000m runner would be operating at about 150 b.p.m. (beats per minute) on his long easy runs. However, there is a minimum pace that needs to be achieved in order to bring about any significant training effect, and if you do only long slow jogs for training you will not stimulate the respiratory/circulatory system enough to bring about any improvement and you will become a good 'long slow runner'!

As an example, a runner who has a resting rate of 50 b.p.m. and a maximum rate of 200 b.p.m. should be training at a pace that will produce a pulse rate of at least 140 b.p.m.

As training thresholds can vary from athlete to athlete, it can be appreciated that training groups at the same pace will benefit some runners but not others. For some the pace will be just right; for others the pace will be too fast resulting in a gradually increasing pulse rate, and these runners will have to slow down; for others, the pace will not be fast enough to raise the pulse to the threshold level. So, in general, if you are going to do steady-state runs with other athletes, try to run with an athlete of a similar level of ability and fitness although this often leads to the runs becoming over-competitive. Avoid this and reserve your competitive instinct mainly for races.

It is sometimes a good idea to check your pulse in the middle of a run and then again at the finish to see whether you are achieving a steady pulse rate at a significant level. You will soon become a good judge of the effort needed to maintain this level over a wide range of distances and will be able to measure improvement by noting how comfortable you feel at a certain pace. A five mile run in 35 minutes may feel hard to the beginner, but this time will soon feel comfortable after a few weeks of regular, intelligent training. As

you improve you will find that you can maintain a given pace for a longer time and with much less effort.

You will also find that you are achieving a lower level pulse plateau at this pace than previously. As soon as this is apparent, then you can step up the pace or length of your runs. Some of the runs can be timed so that you can set yourself training targets and measure improvement. However, you should guard against treating each run as a time-trial, and the ease with which you achieve a time is as useful a measure of improvement as is setting faster times. Much of this steady-state running will be well below full effort, and you should remember that improvement is due to both the quantity and the quality of the training.

The recent vast improvements in the times of long-distance races are, in the main, due to the increased mileages run by athletes, and many apparently mediocre athletes have transformed themselves into good class runners by doubling or trebling their previous weekly mileages. Eighty to one hundred miles each week, much of it at a fairly steady pace, is fairly commonplace now, and some runners have covered even bigger mileages at certain stages in their training. This volume is certainly not necessary for all runners and each athlete should find out for himself the quantity and quality of training that brings about the best results. This can be related to several factors, such as natural ability (runners with this usually get by on less training than less fortunate runners) and mental approach (some people enjoy the shorter, faster runs, while others prefer the longer, slower runs).

It is also important to build up slowly to bigger mileages and not to switch suddenly from running 40 miles a week to 100 miles a week. The body adapts gradually, so training loads should be increased gradually. Quite often, the runner who attempts to increase his training load too quickly (either by quantity or quality) sustains an injury or experiences such constant fatigue that he gives up the experiment after a week or two. When you step up your training mileage, allow a few weeks for your body to adapt before increasing the load again. Maintaining a training load for week after week calls for great concentration and I think that it is valuable now and then to deliberately slip in easier training weeks to allow you to 're-charge your batteries', both physically and mentally.

I mentioned earlier that sessions of varied-pace runs performed aerobically can add variety to the 'steady-state' runs. The important points to remember in this type of session are:

1 The faster stretches are not very fast and only raise the pulse rate a little higher than that achieved on a steady-state run.

2 The slower recovery stretches are quite short so that the pulse rate only falls to a level a little lower than the steady-state level.

With this type of session, the pulse rate may only fluctuate about 20-24 beats and the range involved is probably something in the order of approximately 160/165 b.p.m. after the recovery.

Two typical sessions for a runner whose best time for 10,000 metres is 31 minutes would be:

1 8 x 800 metres in 2 min 20 secs/2min 25 secs with a jog of 100 metres in approximately 40/45 secs between each 800 metres.

2 16 x 300 metres in 53/54 secs interspersed by 50 metre jogs in approximately 30/35 secs.

These sessions do not necessarily have to be run on a track and, in fact, I prefer athletes to run any repetitions over 400 metres on circuits on the roads, in the woods or over the country.

Improving oxygen debt tolerance

Improving oxygen uptake will raise the level at which you can run aerobically, but if the exercise is sufficiently intense and prolonged then it is inevitable that the time will come when the oxygen supply to the working muscles is insufficient to prevent the accumulation of lactic acid. Obviously the longer the distance, the slower the pace and the lower the anaerobic factor, but even on the longer distances there is something to be gained by including some anaerobic work in your training programme. In order to stimulate the body to increase its tolerance to lactic acid, you will need to reproduce the anaerobic effect in training. This means you will have to train at fast speeds to ensure that your oxygen requirements will outstrip your oxygen intake, and training at these high speeds will in turn mean that you cannot maintain the effort for long before slowing down or resting. The training effect is usually achieved by a series of fast runs interspersed with recovery periods. Here are some of the methods used to produce this training

Interval running

The original concept of interval training was for the runner to repeat a set distance in a given time with a fixed recovery jog between. A typical session could be 8 x 200 metres in 30 seconds interspersed by

recovery jogs of 100 metres in one minute. Pulse rates were used to determine the intensity of the fast repetitions and the efficiency of recovery after the jog. Pulses of approximately 180 b.p.m. were looked for after the fast session, going down to 120 b.p.m. after the recovery. The session could be made more difficult by:

1 Increasing the number of fast runs.
2 Increasing the speed of the fast runs.
3 Increasing the distance of the fast runs.
4 Reducing the time spent in recovery.

Although interval training was once regarded primarily as taking place on the track, many athletes now use circuits marked out in the woods, or grass land, or on roads. Another variation to the original concept has been in the use of varying distances during a session, e.g. 2 x 400m,

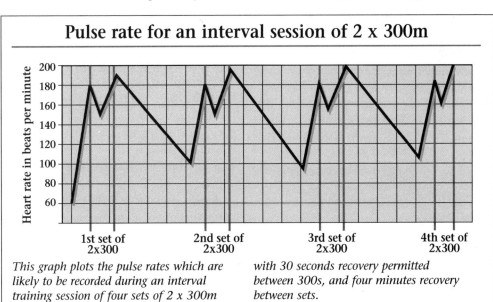

Pulse rate for an interval session of 2 x 300m

This graph plots the pulse rates which are likely to be recorded during an interval training session of four sets of 2 x 300m *with 30 seconds recovery permitted between 300s, and four minutes recovery between sets.*

4 x 600m, 2 x 800m with appropriate recovery runs between.

A further variation used by many of the long-distance runners that I have coached is to split up the session into a series of sets, such as 4 sets of 2 x 1000 metres, with a very short recovery between each pair of fast runs, then a longer recovery between sets. The training effect on the heart in this type of session is shown on page 83 and should be compared with that produced by a more traditional type of interval session (see below).

To my mind, it is essential that during interval training the fast runs and recovery jogs are accurately timed, and that pulse rates are checked occasionally to ensure that the correct effect is being achieved.

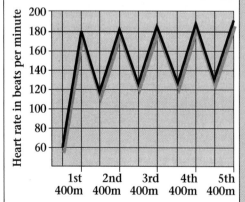

Pulse rate for an interval session of 5 x 400m

This graph shows the pulse rates which are likely to be recorded for an athlete during an interval training session of 5 x 400m, allowing a 200m recovery jog between each.

The session is not producing much in the way of training effect if the pulse is not raised sufficiently high after the fast runs or if too much recovery time is allowed. However, insufficient recovery time will not allow the athlete to maintain a good quality in the fast runs.

As your body adapts, so you will find that the sessions become easier and to continue the training improvement there must be some progression by intensifying the session. I like to think of distance runners improving the quality of sessions in the winter by increasing the number of runs or the distance of the fast runs, and in the summer by increasing the speed of the fast runs or by reducing the recovery times. However, to increase the speed of the fast runs may mean having to allow longer recoveries or reducing quantity. Reducing the recovery time may mean having to decrease the numbers of fast runs or splitting the session up into sets.

The distance and the pace of the fast runs should be related to the athlete's racing distance as this is the physiological effect he is trying to stimulate the body to become adapted to, so I suggest:
1 A variation in distances from 200 to 1000m.
2 A pace faster than that covered in the same segment of a race. For example, during a 5000 metre race run in 14 min 30 secs a runner would cover each 800 metres in approximately 2 min 20 secs. His training pace during 800 metre intervals should be at least 5 seconds faster than this rate.

3 Total distance covered during the fast runs in an interval session should be at least two-thirds of the racing distance and no more than one-third in excess of racing distance, e.g. for 10,000 metre runner, 4 sets of 3 x 1000 metres, or 4 x 3000 metres.

Repetition running

In this type of anaerobic training, the athlete does fast sustained runs at fairly longish distances, and because of the fast pace and the distances covered he needs a complete rest between the runs in order to recover adequately. The athlete cannot be expected to run many of these repetitions and some suggested sessions for varying distances might be:

1 5000 metres – 5 x 800 metres at about 5 seconds per lap faster than racing pace with 4/5 minutes rest between each.
2 10,000 metres – 3 x 3000 metres, again at faster than racing pace with 7/8 minutes rest between each.

Quality is the important factor with these runs so the numbers will be small, the pace fast and the recovery long.

Fartlek (speed play)

This is the Swedish term used to describe informal fast and slow running, usually over hilly terrain such as woods, golf courses and parkland. The athlete runs for a period of time rather than for a set distance, and during the run he varies the pace according to the terrain and his state of fitness. Before the run, he will probably visualize the route he is going to cover and have a rough idea about which stretches are going to be run fast and which are to be used for recovery. The pace can vary from a quick knee-lifting burst up a short steep hill to a long, sustained stride over a level stretch of country. The jogs between the fast stretches should be just sufficient to allow partial recovery, so the length and the pace of these jogs will also vary.

Although, to a degree, the athlete runs as he pleases, he should ensure that there is a good variety of running at different speeds and over varying distances and that the session is not over-loaded with jogging stretches. Progression is necessary to enable the runner to increase the quality of the fast stretches and reduce the amount of time spent jogging as he gets fitter.

To get the best results out of a fartlek session calls for strong self-discipline, and the inexperienced runner may spend too much time jogging. If you are new to fartlek, you should do a few sessions with an experienced runner in order to get the feel of what is required and from then on should work out alone, becoming your own judge as to the intensity of the session. You must be honest with yourself and train hard without supervision. This is a very natural and stimulating form of training, but to produce good results calls for the same concentration as a formal interval session. I suggest a minimum of 45 minutes' fartlek for the 800 or 1500m runner, building up to 90 minutes' running for the 10km runner.

Race practice

As the name suggests, this form of training tries to reproduce race sensations, both mentally and physically, and is of most value to the 5000 and 10,000 metre runners. Races are very rarely run at a level pace throughout, so I think it useful to reproduce these pace variations during training sessions. It is quite common for surges to occur during the middle of a race or for the race to get progressively faster. Some typical training exercises that would reproduce race feelings are as follows:

1 5000 metre runner capable of 15 min 30 secs

6 x 1200 metres – 1st 400 in 75 secs; 2nd 400 in 70 secs; 3rd 400 in 75 secs – 1 lap jog recovery between each 1200 metres

2 10,000 metre runner capable of 31 mins

4 x 1600 metres – 1st 400 in 79 secs; 2nd 400 in 77 secs; 3rd 400 in 75 secs; 4th 400 in 73 secs – 1 lap jog recovery between each 1200 metres

The relationship between training plans and competition dates

Many runners want to compete regularly during the track season and it is necessary to fit in regular racing that influences the make-up of a training schedule during the 'Racing Phase'. Other runners plan their schedules with a view to building up to a few high-level performances at infrequent intervals. The first option means that if you opt to race every week, then you must scale down weekly training accordingly so that you go to each race feeling fresh. The second option gives you more scope to develop the quality and quantity of your training. Certain weeks can be regarded as purely training weeks, whereas others can be treated as race-preparation weeks.

You will now appreciate that training schedules, while incorporating the principles of exercise physiology, should also be tailored to individual needs. This sets the seemingly impossible task of presenting schedules without knowing the individual characteristics of every runner who will read this chapter. What I have done is to suggest training programmes for different types of runners, using training principles to suit certain individuals. From these examples, you can design your own schedules that will take into account your personal requirements. I suggest that you ask yourself the following questions:

1 What does the event require?
2 What have I got to offer?
3 What do I need to do to make question one match up to question two?

Although the schedules that follow are meant as examples, they are not theoretical exercises, and they have been used to good effect by some of the people I have coached.

Schedule A - 800m

This runner has a personal best of 2 mins 4 secs for 800 metres and is aiming to improve to 2 mins 00 secs in the coming year. He can only train once a day during the week but can devote more time at weekends, and is within easy access of good facilities, such as well-lit roads in the autumn and winter months, an all-weather track and woods and parkland. The schedule is based on the concept of three training phases:

1 The endurance phase.
2 The pre-competition phase.
3 The summer competition phase.

The endurance phase

This is a period of approximately five months from October to March, (in the northern hemisphere) and during this phase your main objective is to improve oxygen uptake. However, during this period a small percentage of training will be devoted to the retention of speed, technique and speed endurance. As your endurance level improves, you should take part occasionally in cross-country or road races. These will provide interest and a challenge and will reflect the improvement in your aerobic energy system.

This period should be regarded as a period of quantity rather than quality training. The success of the phase will be measured by the week after week of gradually improved training which has been accomplished rather than by the quality of a few individual sessions. The ability to perform high-quality work in the next stage will, to a large degree, depend upon the foundation of endurance that you have achieved in this first phase.

October – weeks 1 & 2

Sunday	- 6 miles easy run
Monday	- 5 miles easy run
Tuesday	- rest day
Wednesday	- 12 x 100m relaxed strides; 100m slow jog between each stride
Thursday	- 6 miles easy run
Friday	- rest day
Saturday	- 4 miles fastish run

October – weeks 3 & 4

Sunday	- 7 miles easy run
Monday	- 5 miles steady run
Tuesday	- rest day
Wednesday	- 10 x 150m relaxed stride; 100m jog between each stride
Thursday	- 6 miles easy run
Friday	- rest day
Saturday	- 5 miles steady run. Follow this run with 8 x 60m fast strides – walk back slowly between each stride

November – weeks 1, 2 & 3

Sunday	- 7 miles easy run
Monday	- 5 miles steady run
Tuesday	- 5 repetitions around a fairly flat circuit measuring between 1000m and 1200m

Training tip

Use a circuit around the roads, or go out in the country rather than run on the track. These runs should be fairly relaxed; allow a recovery time of 1 minute. As a guide, your pulse rate should be about 160 beats per minute at the end of each repetition and should go down to about 130 beats per minute at the end of the recovery period.

Wednesday	- rest day
Thursday	- 6 miles steady run
Friday	- 5 miles easy run
Saturday am	- 10 relaxed strides over 150m; 100m jog between each stride
Saturday pm	- 4 miles fastish run

November – week 4

This is a recuperation week and is intended to allow the body to recover and adapt before moving on to harder training.

Sunday	- 5 miles easy run
Monday	- 5 miles easy run
Tuesday	- rest day
Wednesday	- 8 x 200m relaxed strides; 200m jog between each run
Thursday	- 5 miles easy run
Friday	- rest day
Saturday	- 5 miles easy run

December – weeks 1, 2 & 3

Sunday	- 8 miles easy run
Monday	- 6 miles steady run
Tuesday	- 6 x 1000/1200m circuit. Maintain the pace set in October but reduce the recovery time to 30 seconds.

Note: With such a short recovery time it is important to ensure that the first two or three repetitions are not run too quickly.

Wednesday	- rest day
Thursday	- 6 miles steady run
Friday	- 8 miles easy run
Saturday am	- Track: 8 x 200m (aim for 31/32 seconds). These runs should be quite fast but relaxed. Jog 200m between each run
pm	- 5 miles fastish run

December – week 4; January – weeks 1 & 2

Sunday am	- 10 miles easy run
pm	- 8 x 100m relaxed stride; 100m walk between each run
Monday	- 6 miles steady run
Tuesday	- 6 x 1000/1200m circuit – maintain the 30 seconds recovery period but try to increase the pace a little
Wednesday	- 8 miles easy run
Thursday	- 6 miles steady run
Friday	- rest day
Saturday am	- 10 fast but relaxed strides over 200m (aim for 30/31 seconds); jog 200m between each run
pm	- 6 miles fastish run

Note: Every other week substitute a cross-country or 5 mile/10 km road race for Saturday's training.

January – weeks 3 & 4; February – week 1

Sunday am	- 10 miles easy run
pm	- 10 x 150m relaxed stride; walk back slowly between each stride
Monday	- 6 miles steady run
Tuesday	- 6 x 1000/1200m circuit. Have 1 minute recovery between each repetition
Wednesday	- 8 miles easy run

Training tip

Find a circuit that's a little more difficult to run around than the one used previously. I suggest a course that contains two fairly steep hills or one longish (300m) shallow hill.

Thursday	- 6 miles run split up – 4½ miles steady, ½ mile easy, 1 mile fast
Friday	- rest day
Saturday am	- 2 sets of 5 x 200m (aim for 29/30 seconds); jog 100m between each 200m, then 400m jog between each set
pm	- 6 miles steady run

Note: Alternate the Saturday training sessions with a cross-country or road race.

February – weeks 2 & 3

Sunday am	- 10 miles easy run
pm	- 8 x 150m relaxed stride – walk back slowly between each run
Monday	- 6 miles steady run
Tuesday	- 6 x 1000/1200m circuit – maintain the pace used previously but shorten the recovery to 30 seconds
Wednesday	- 8 miles easy run
Thursday	- 6 miles run split up – 4 miles steady, ½ mile easy 1½ miles fast
Friday	- rest day
Saturday am	- 3 sets of 4 x 200m (aim for 29/30 seconds); jog 200m between each fast repetition, then 400m jog between the sets
pm	- 40 minutes Fartlek

February – week 4

This is a recuperation week and follows a similar pattern to the training quoted for the 4th week of November. This week also marks the end of the endurance phase.

The pre-competition phase

During this phase the emphasis moves to speed and speed/endurance, but there is still a considerable element of endurance in the training. The inclusion of hill-work introduces the strength factor into the training plan. I prefer to see leg-strength gained in this way rather than by the use of static weight-training exercises.

This phase of training becomes quite intensive and you must ensure that you always warm up and do some mobility exercises before the high-quality sessions. There is a greater risk of injury in this period, so at the first signs of an injury, consult an experienced physiotherapist. Massage for relaxation following intensive sessions can also be valuable.

March – weeks 1, 2 & 3

Sunday am	- 10 miles easy run
pm	- 8 x 150m relaxed stride – walk back slowly between each stride
Monday	- 4 miles fastish run
Tuesday	- 5 x 1000/1200m circuit. Return to the flatter circuit and run these at a good pace with 2 minutes recovery between each fast repetition
Wednesday	- 8 miles steady run
Thursday	- Track: 5 x 600m (aim for 93/94 seconds). Jog 400m between each repetition. Have 20 minutes rest, then follow with 6

x 60m sprint. Walk back slowly between each sprint

Friday	- rest day
Saturday am	- 4 miles easy run
pm	- 8 repetitions up a shallow/medium hill (about 350/400m long). Jog down slowly between each repetition

Training tip

These runs are carried out to improve leg-strength so it is important to maintain a normal length stride. You would probably run the hill quicker by shortening your stride, but this would not develop leg-strength.

March – week 4; April – weeks 1 & 2

Sunday am	- 8 miles steady run
pm	- 8 x 150m relaxed strides – usual recovery
Monday	- 6 miles run split up: 4½ miles steady, ½ mile easy, 1 mile fast
Tuesday	- 5 x 1000/1200m circuit. Use the hillier circuit and try to do the repetitions quite fast. Have a 3 minute recovery between each run
Wednesday	- 6 miles steady run
Thursday	- Track: 4 x 600m (aim for 90/91 seconds). Jog 600m between each repetition. 20 minutes rest, then 8 x 80m sprint. Walk back slowly between each sprint
Friday	- rest day
Saturday	- 8 repetitions up the 350/400m shallow/medium hill. Try to run these faster than previously

while maintaining the good length of stride. Jog back down slowly between each repetition

April – weeks 3 & 4; May – week 1

Sunday am	- 8 miles steady run
pm	- 8 x 100m acceleration runs, i.e. start off each run striding easily, then gradually speed up until you are sprinting at the end of each repetition. Walk back slowly
Monday	- 6 miles run split up: 4 miles steady
Tuesday	- Track: 1000m (aim for 2 minutes 40 seconds); 600m jog; 600m (aim for 93 seconds); 600m jog; 2 x 400m (aim for 60 seconds); 400m jog after each repetition, 3 x 200m (aim for 28 seconds); 200m jog between each repetition
Wednesday	- 6 miles steady run
Thursday	- Track: 6 x 400m (aim for 58/59 seconds); 400m jog between repetitions
Friday	- rest day
Saturday am	- 4 miles easy run
pm	- Track: 4 sets 3 x 200m (aim for 29/30 seconds); 1 minute rest between each 200m; 1 lap jog between each set

May – weeks 2, 3 & 4

Sunday am	- 6 miles steady run
pm	- 8 x 80m fast runs up a steep hill. Maintain a good length stride. Walk back slowly between each run
Monday	- 6 miles steady run

Tuesday	- similar session to previous 3 weeks. Try to speed up the times of the repetitions
Wednesday	- 8 miles easy run
Thursday	- Track: 8 x 300m (aim for 42/43 seconds); 500m jog between each repetition
Friday	- rest day
Saturday am	- 4 miles easy run
pm	- 4 sets: 300m fast (44 seconds); 1 minute rest; 200m fast (28 seconds); 1 minute rest; 100m fast (13 seconds). Have 1.5 laps jog between each set

May – last 4 days; June – first 3 days

This is a recuperation week. Follow the plan set down for similar weeks in November and February.

The competition season

If you are following this Training plan, then you probably like to race quite frequently, so I have devised a 3-week cycle of training between important races. At the beginning of each cycle, the training is still quite intensive albeit lower in quantity. Towards the end of each cycle, there is a reduction of effort so that you are fresh for important races. As this period will last approximately 15 weeks, it means that you will have 10 races. Two of these races would be at 1500m, two at 400m and six at the chosen distance of 800m.

First and second 3-week cycles

Week 1

Sunday am	- 10 miles steady run
pm	- 6 x 100m relaxed stride; walk back recovery

Monday	- 5 mile run split: 4 miles steady, ½ mile easy, ½ mile fast
Tuesday	- 4 x 600m. The first 400m should be in 61/62 seconds, then the last 200m as fast as possible. Have 7/8 minutes recovery between each repetition
Wednesday	- 6 miles easy run
Thursday	- 4 x 1000/1200m flat circuit. Run these quite fast with 4/5 minutes recovery jog between each repetition
Friday	- rest day
Saturday am	- 4 miles easy run
pm	- 8 x 300m (aim for 41/42 seconds); 400m jog between fast runs. Have 20 minutes rest, then run 4 x 100m acceleration strides. Walk back between each stride

Week 2

Sunday am	- 8 miles easy run
pm	- 8 x 100m relaxed stride; walk back recovery
Monday	- 3 x 500m (aim for 73 seconds); 600m slow jog between each repetition; 20 minutes rest, then 4 x 150m sprint. Walk back recovery
Tuesday	- 6 miles easy run
Wednesday	- 6 x 400m (split these up: 300m steady, 100m fast); 600m jog for recovery
Thursday	- 5 miles steady run
Friday	- rest day
Saturday	- 1500m race

Week 3

Sunday am	- 6 miles easy run
pm	- 8 x 100m relaxed stride; walk back recovery

Monday	- 4 x 300m fast; 7/8 minutes rest between each 300m; 20 minutes rest, then 6 x 60m acceleration run. Walk back recovery
Tuesday	- 6 miles steady run
Wednesday	- 6 x 200m fast, but relaxed strides on grass; 200m jog for recovery
Thursday	- 4 miles easy run
Friday	- rest day
Saturday	- 800m race

Third and fourth 3-week cycles

Week 1

Sunday	am	- 10 miles steady run
	pm	- 8 x 100m relaxed stride; walk back recovery
Monday		- 6 miles run split: 4½ miles steady, ½ mile easy, 1 mile fast
Tuesday		- 4 sets: 300m (43 seconds); 1 minute recovery; 200m (27 seconds); 1 minute recovery; 100m (12.5 seconds). Have 8 minutes rest between sets
Wednesday		- 6 miles steady run
Thursday		- 5 x 1000/1200m flat circuit – run quite relaxed with 1 minute jog for recovery
Friday		- rest day
Saturday		- 1 x 1000m (2 minutes 36 seconds); 8 minutes recovery. 2 x 500m (75 seconds); 8 minutes recovery. 4 x 200m (28/29 seconds); 200m recovery jog

Week 2

Sunday	am	- 8 miles easy run
	pm	- 8 x 100m relaxed stride; walk back recovery

Monday		- 6 x 300m (41/42 seconds); 400m jog for recovery; 20 minutes rest, then 6 x 60m acceleration runs – walk back recovery
Tuesday		- 5 miles steady run
Wednesday		- 6 x 150m sprint – walk back recovery
Thursday		- 4 miles easy run
Friday		- rest day
Saturday		- 400m race

Week 3

Sunday	am	- 6 miles easy run
	pm	- 6 x 100m relaxed stride – walk back recovery
Monday		- 2 x 500m very fast; 7/8 minutes recovery between each run; 20 minutes rest, then 6 x 60m acceleration runs – walk back recovery
Tuesday		- 6 miles steady run
Wednesday		- 6 x 200m fast, but relaxed on grass; 200m jog for recovery
Thursday		- 4 miles easy run
Friday		- rest day
Saturday		- 800m race

Fifth 3-week cycle

Week 1

Sunday	am	- 10 miles steady run
	pm	- 6 x 100m relaxed stride – walk back recovery
Monday		- 5 miles easy run
Tuesday		- 4 sets: 300m fast; 1 minute recovery; 300m fast – 7/8 minutes recovery between each set
Wednesday		- 6 miles steady run
Thursday		- 8 x 150m sprint – walk back recovery
Friday		- rest day

Saturday am	- 4 miles easy run
pm	- 1 x 1000m (2 minutes 34 seconds); 8 minutes recovery
	2 x 500m (73 seconds); 8 minutes recovery; 4 x 200m (28 seconds); 200m jog for recovery

Week 2

Sunday am	- 8 miles easy run
pm	- 8 x 100m relaxed stride; walk back recovery
Monday	- 4 x 500m (run the first 400m relaxed in 60 seconds, then speed up over the last 100m); 8 minutes rest between each repetition
Tuesday	- 5 miles easy run
Wednesday	- 8 x 200m (these runs are split up: 100m stride; 100m sprint); jog 200m for recovery

Thursday -	4 miles easy run
Friday	- rest day
Saturday	- 800m race

Week 3

Sunday am	- 6 miles easy run
pm	- 8 x 100m relaxed stride – walk back relaxed
Monday	- 3 x 300m very fast; 8 minutes rest between each run; 20 minutes rest, then 6 x 60m sprint – walk back relaxed
Tuesday	- 6 miles steady run
Wednesday	- 6 x 200m fast, but relaxed on grass; 200m jog for recovery
Thursday	- 4 miles easy run
Friday	- rest day
Saturday	- 800m race

Schedule B: 1500m

This plan is for a runner who has a personal best of 4 minutes 4 seconds for 1500m and is aiming to improve to 3 minutes 56 seconds in the coming year. Once again, he can train only once a day but can do more at weekends.

The endurance phase

In this period, I suggest that you follow the same programme as that detailed earlier for the 800m runner. However, as you possess more endurance, then I would expect the steady-state runs to be a little faster and slightly longer than those used by the 800m runner. The recuperation weeks would be similar to those used in Schedule A.

Pre-competition period

March – weeks 1, 2 & 3

Sunday am	- 10 miles easy run
pm	- 8 x 150m relaxed stride – walk back recovery
Monday	- 6 miles fastish run
Tuesday	- 6 x 1000/1200m circuit. Use the flatter circuit, increase the pace slightly; allow a 2 minute recovery jog between each repetition

Wednesday	- 8 miles steady run
Thursday	- Track: 12 x 400m (65/66 seconds); jog 300m between each repetition; take 20 minutes rest, then sprint 8 x 80m – walk back slowly between each run
Friday	- rest day
Saturday	- 6 repetitions up a 500/600m shallow hill. Make sure you keep a good stride length to benefit leg-strength. Jog back fairly quickly between each repetition

March – week 4; April – weeks 1 & 2

Sunday	am - 10 miles steady run
	pm - 8 x 150m relaxed stride – walk back recovery
Monday	- 7 miles run split up: 5½ miles steady, ½ mile easy, 1 mile fast
Tuesday	- 6 x 1000/1200m circuit. Use the hillier circuit and run these repetitions quite fast. Jog for 3 minutes recovery between each circuit
Wednesday	- 8 miles steady run
Thursday	- 8 x 600m (97/98 seconds); jog 400m between each repetition. After 20 minutes rest, sprint 8 x 60m; walk back slowly between each sprint
Friday	- rest day
Saturday	am - 4 miles easy run
	pm - 6 repetitions up the 500/600m hill. Try to run these a little quicker than previously without shortening your stride. Use the same quick jog down between each repetition

April – week 4; May – week 1

| Sunday | am - 12 miles easy run |

Sunday	pm - 8 x 100m acceleration runs – walk back recovery
Monday	- 7 miles run split up: 5 miles steady, ½ mile easy, 1½ miles fast
Tuesday	- Track: 1 x 1200m (3 minutes 16 seconds); 800m jog; 800m (2 minutes 9 seconds); 600m jog; 2 x 500m (81 seconds); 500m jog; 2 x 300m (48 seconds) – 300m jog between each 300m
Wednesday	- 8 miles steady run
Thursday	- 4 x 600m (94 seconds); 400m jog between each repetition. Have 20 minutes rest, then sprint 6 x 100m with a slow walk back between each sprint
Friday	- rest day
Saturday	am - 4 sets of 2 x 400m fast (62 seconds); 1 minute rest between each 400m; have 7/8 minutes recovery between each set
	pm - 5 miles easy run

May – middle 3 weeks

Sunday	am - 10 miles steady run
	pm - 8 x 100m relaxed stride – walk back recovery
Monday	- 7 miles easy run
Tuesday	- Track: 600m (95/96 seconds); 600m jog; 800m (2 minutes 7 seconds); 800m jog; 1000m (2 minutes 40 seconds); 800 jog; 1200m (3 minutes 12 seconds); 1000m jog; 400m (60/61 seconds). Have 20 minutes rest, then run 6 x 80m fast strides. Walk back recovery
Wednesday	- 8 miles steady run
Thursday	- Track: 4 x 500m (75 seconds); 600m jog between each repetition. After 20 minutes rest, sprint 6 x 60m – walk back recovery

Friday	- rest day	
Saturday	am	- 4 miles easy run
	pm	- 5 sets 2 x 300m fast (45 seconds); 1 minute rest between each 300m; 7/8 minutes rest between each set

May – last 4 days; June – first 3 days

This is a recuperation week (see plan used by 800m runner) and marks the end of the pre-competition phase.

Competition period

Again, I have assumed that you wish to race frequently, so I have suggested a 3-week cycle of training between important races. The phase lasts approximately 15 weeks and means that you will have two races at 800m, two races at 3000m and six races at 1500m or 1 mile.

First and second 3-week cycles

Week 1

Sunday	am	- 10 miles steady run
	pm	- 6 x 100m relaxed stride – walk back recovery
Monday		- 6 x 100/200m flat circuit – quite relaxed but with just 30 seconds recovery between each repetition
Tuesday		- 8 miles steady run
Wednesday		- Track: 4 x 400m (62 seconds); 400m jog recovery; 4 x 200m (29 seconds); 200m jog recovery
Thursday		- 6 miles easy run
Friday		- rest day
Saturday		- 3000m race

Week 2

Sunday	am	- 8 miles easy run
Saturday	pm	- 4 miles easy run
Monday		- 6 miles run split: 4½ miles steady, ½ mile easy, 1 mile fast
Tuesday		- 6 x 500m (78 seconds); 500m jog recovery; 20 minutes rest, then 6 x 150m acceleration runs – walk back recovery
Wednesday		- 8 miles steady run
Thursday		- 4 sets 2 x 300m (44 seconds); 1 minute rest between each 300m; 7/8 minutes recovery between sets
Friday		- rest day
Saturday	am	- 5 miles easy run
	pm	- 4 x 1000/1200m hilly circuit – run these quite fast, with 2 minutes jog for recovery

Week 3

Sunday	am	- 10 miles steady run
	pm	- 6 x 100m relaxed stride; walk back recovery
Monday		- 2 x 800m (2 minutes 5 seconds); 10 minutes rest between each run; 20 minutes rest, then run 6 x 80m acceleration runs. Walk back recovery
Tuesday		- 6 miles steady run
Wednesday		- 6 x 200m on grass – fast but relaxed; 200m jog between each 200m
Thursday		- 5 miles easy run
Friday		- rest day
Saturday		- 1500m race

Third and fourth 3-week cycles

Week 1

Sunday	am	- 8 miles steady run
	pm	- 4 x 150m relaxed stride – walk back recovery
Monday		- 6 miles steady run

Tuesday	- 4 x 600m: 1st 200m 34 seconds; 2nd 200m 31 seconds; 3rd 200m 34 seconds – 7/8 minutes recovery between each repetition. 20 minutes rest followed by 6 x 100m relaxed stride – walk back recovery
Wednesday	- 8 miles easy run
Thursday	- 9 x 400m (61/62 seconds); 300m jog recovery
Friday	- rest day
Saturday am	- 4 miles easy run
pm	- 6 x 1000/1200m flat circuit. Run these relaxed with 1 minute recovery between each run

Week 2

Sunday am	- 10 miles easy run
pm	- 8 x 100m acceleration runs – walk back recovery
Monday	- 4 x 300m very fast; 8 minutes rest between each 300m
Tuesday	- 6 miles steady run
Wednesday	- 8 x 200m – split these runs into 100m stride; 100m sprint. Have 200m jog for recovery
Thursday	- 5 miles easy run
Friday	- rest day
Saturday	- 800m race

Week 3

Sunday am	- 8 miles easy run
pm	- 3 miles easy run
Monday	- 3 x 400m (60 seconds); 400m jog for recovery. 3 x 200m (28 seconds); 200m jog for recovery
Tuesday	- 6 miles easy run
Wednesday	- 1 x 1000m (2 minutes 40 seconds); 3 laps jog for recovery. 1 x 600m (92 seconds); 20 minutes rest followed by 5 x 60m relaxed stride; walk back recovery

Thursday	- 4 miles easy run
Friday	- rest day
Saturday	- 1500 race

Fifth 3-week cycle

Week 1

Sunday am	- 8 miles easy run
pm	- 6 x 150m relaxed stride – walk back recovery
Monday	- 6 miles steady run
Tuesday	- 9 x 400m (60 seconds); 300 jog for recovery
Wednesday	- 5 miles run split up: 3½ miles steady, ½ mile easy, 1 mile fast
Thursday	- 3 x 500m (75 seconds); 8 minutes rest between each run. 20 minutes rest followed by 6 x 60m sprint; walk back recovery
Friday	- rest day
Saturday	- 4 x 1000/1200 hilly circuit. Run quite quickly with 2 minutes jog for recovery. 20 minutes rest, then 6 x 60m acceleration runs; walk back recovery

Week 2

Sunday am	- 10 miles steady run
pm	- 8 x 100m relaxed stride – walk back recovery
Monday	- 4 x 600m (1st 400m in 64 seconds, then 200m as fast as possible); 2 laps slow jog for recovery. 20 minutes rest, then 6 x 60m relaxed stride; walk back recovery
Tuesday	- 8 miles steady run
Wednesday	- 3 x 400m (59 seconds); 400m recovery jog 3 x 200m (27 seconds); 200m recovery jog
Thursday	- 5 miles easy run
Friday	- rest day
Saturday	- 1500m or 1 mile race

Week 3

Sunday	am	- 6 miles easy run
	pm	- 4 miles easy run
Monday		- 3 x 800m (2 minutes 7 seconds); 3 laps jog between each run
Tuesday		- 5 miles steady run

Wednesday		- 5 miles easy run
Thursday		- 6 x 200m on grass, fast, but relaxed; 200m jog for recovery
Friday		- rest day
Saturday		- 1500m or 1 mile race

Schedule C – 5000/10,000m

This schedule is aimed at runners with a personal best of 14 minutes 00 seconds for 5000m, and 29 minutes 20 seconds for 10,000m, and who are aiming to improve these times to 13 minutes 45 seconds and 28 minutes 40 seconds respectively and can train twice on most days. Although the first period is used as the main endurance phase, you may also wish to run well in the major cross-country races that occur towards the end of this period.

Endurance phase

October – weeks 1 & 2

Sunday	- 6 miles easy run
Monday	- 6 miles easy run
Tuesday	- 8 miles easy run
Wednesday	- rest day
Thursday	- 6 miles easy run
Friday	- 6 miles easy run
Saturday	- 8 miles easy run

October – weeks 3 & 4

Sunday		- 8 miles easy run
Monday	am	- 5 miles easy run
	pm	- 6 miles steady run
Tuesday		- 10 miles easy run
Wednesday		- rest day

Thursday		- 8 miles steady run
Friday	am	- 5 miles easy run
	pm	- 6 miles steady run
Saturday	am	- 5 miles easy run
	pm	- 6 miles Fartlek

November – weeks 1, 2 & 3

Sunday	am	- 10 miles steady run
	pm	- 10 x 100m relaxed stride – walk back recovery
Monday		- 8 miles steady run
Tuesday	am	- 5 miles easy run
	pm	- 5 x 1 mile repetitions round a fairly flat road or country circuit; 2 minutes jog for recovery
Wednesday		- 10 miles easy run
Thursday	am	- 5 miles easy run
	pm	- 7 miles run split: 5 miles steady, ½ mile easy, 1½ miles fast
Friday		- rest day
Saturday	am	- 5 miles easy run
	pm	- 8 repetitions up a shallow hill – 500/600m long. Maintain a normal stride length on the uphill runs. Jog down quickly after each repetition

Note: In the third week, substitute a low-level road or cross-country race for this session.

November – week 4

This is a recuperation week. You should run 6 miles easily on each day except for Tuesday and Friday which are rest days.

December – weeks 1, 2 & 3

Sunday	am	- 12 miles steady run
	pm	- 10 x 100m relaxed stride – walk back recovery
Monday		- 8 miles steady run
Tuesday	am	- 5 miles easy run
	pm	- 5 x 1 mile repetitions. Maintain the pace set previously but reduce the recovery to 1 minute
Wednesday	am	- 3 miles easy run
	pm	- 10 miles steady run

Thursday	am	- 6 miles easy run
	pm	- 7 miles run split up: 4½ miles steady, ½ mile easy, 2 miles fast
Friday		- rest day
Saturday	am	- 5 miles easy run
	pm	- 8 repetitions up the shallow 500/600m hill. Run these a little faster then previously but maintain the good technique. Retain the same recovery time

Note: In the third week, drop this session and substitute a medium-level road or cross-country race.

December – week 4; January – weeks 1, 2 & 3

Sunday	am	- 12 miles steady run
	pm	- 4 miles easy run
Monday	am	- 4 miles easy run
	pm	- 8 miles steady run
Tuesday	am	- 5 miles easy run
	pm	- 2 x 2 mile repetitions around a flat road circuit; 3 minute jog for recovery. 4 x 1 mile repetitions around a flat road circuit; 1 minute jog for recovery
Wednesday		- 10 miles steady run
Thursday	am	- 5 miles easy run
	pm	- 6 miles fastish run. On alternate weeks make this a 5 miles easy run

You can train in most weather conditions in the winter months, even in snow. Be sure to wrap up warmly and wear a hat if possible, as most body heat is lost through the head. Take special care on ice and slippery surfaces; always wear studded running shoes to get a good grip.

Friday		- rest day
Saturday	am	- 4 miles easy run
	pm	- 8 repetitions round a fairly hilly cross-country or parkland circuit that is about 1000/1200m long. These repetitions should be fairly relaxed as the recovery time between repetitions should be kept to 30 seconds.

Note: On alternate weeks, substitute a good quality cross-country race for this session.

January – week 4; February – week 1

Sunday	am	- 15 miles easy run
	pm	- 3 miles easy run
Monday	am	- 5 miles easy run
	pm	- 6 miles steady run
Tuesday	am	- 5 miles easy run
	pm	- 2 x 2 miles repetitions – maintain pace but reduce recovery time to 2 minutes. 2 x 1 mile repetitions – increase pace a little, but maintain recovery at 1 minute; 1 x 2 mile repetition – relaxed pace but try to speed up over the last 800m
Wednesday		- 12 miles steady run
Thursday	am	- 4 miles easy run
	pm	- 8 miles steady run
Friday		- 4 miles easy run
Saturday	am	- 5 miles easy run
	pm	- 8 repetitions round the 1000/1200m cross-country circuit. Try to increase the pace a little but maintain the recovery at 30 seconds.

Note: On alternate weeks substitute a good-quality cross-country race for this session.

February – weeks 2 & 3

Sunday	am	- 13 miles easy run
	pm	- 4 miles easy run
Monday	am	- 5 miles easy run
	pm	- 6 miles steady run
Tuesday	am	- 5 miles easy run
	pm	- 2 x 2 mile repetitions – maintain pace but reduce recovery to 1 minute. 3 x 1 mile repetitions. Try to run each repetition a little faster than the one before. 2 minutes jog for recovery
Wednesday		- 10 miles steady run
Thursday	am	- 4 miles easy run
	pm	- 8 miles steady run
Friday		- 12 x 100m relaxed stride – walk back recovery
Saturday	am	- 5 miles easy run
Saturday	pm	- 45 minutes Fartlek

February – week 4

Sunday	am	- 12 miles easy run
	pm	- 3 miles easy run
Monday	am	- 5 miles easy run
	pm	- 6 miles easy run
Tuesday	am	- 3 miles easy run
	pm	- 3 x 1 mile road repetitions. Run these fast, but relaxed. Have 2 minutes recovery jog between each repetition
Wednesday		- 6 miles steady run
Thursday		- 4 miles easy run
Friday		- rest day
Saturday		- high-quality cross-country race

March – week 1

Sunday	am	- 8 miles easy run

Sunday	pm	- 8 x 100m relaxed stride – walk back recovery
Monday	am	- 4 miles easy run
	pm	- 6 miles steady run
Tuesday	am	- 4 miles easy run
	pm	- 3 x 2 miles road repetitions. Run these quite fast but relaxed. Recovery jog for 2 minutes between each repetition
Wednesday		- 8 miles steady run
Thursday	am	- 4 miles easy run
	pm	- 3 miles fastish run
Friday		- 4 miles easy run
Saturday	am	- 5 miles easy run
	pm	- 8 repetitions around the flat cross-country circuit. Keep the runs relaxed and the recovery down to 30 seconds

March – weeks 2 & 3

Use the same programme as that quoted for the middle 2 weeks in February.

March – week 4

Use the same schedule as the one used for the last week in February.

March – last 3 days; April – first 4 days

This is a recuperation week and follows the same pattern as the schedule given for the 4th week in November.

Pre-track competition phase

April – weeks 1 & 2

Sunday	am	- 12 miles easy run
	pm	- 8 x 100m relaxed stride – walk back recovery

Repetition running is an effective form of anaerobic training, and during the pre-track competition phase you must include some of this track work to increase your speed.

Monday	am	- 5 miles easy run
	pm	- 6 miles steady run
Tuesday	am	- 5 miles easy run
	pm	- Track: 6 x 600m (aim for 96 seconds); 200m slow jog between each repetition. After 20 minutes rest, run 4 x 200m quite relaxed with 200m jog between each repetition

Wednesday		- 10 miles steady run
Thursday	am	- 5 miles easy run
	pm	- 7 miles run split up: 5 miles steady, ½ mile easy, 1½ miles fast
Friday		- 6 miles easy run
Saturday	am	- 4 miles easy run
	pm	- Track: 1 x 400m; 1 x 600m; 1 x 800m; 1 x 1000m; 1 x 1200m; 1 x 1500m. Aim to run all these at 66 seconds, 400m pace. Have 2 minutes recovery jog after the first 3 repetitions, then 3 minutes jog after the remaining repetitions. After 20 minutes rest run 2 x 200m quite fast with a 200m slow jog for recovery

April – weeks 3 & 4; May – week 1

Sunday	am	- 12 miles steady run
	pm	- 8 x 100m relaxed stride – walk back recovery
Monday	am	- 5 miles easy run
	pm	- 7 miles steady run
Tuesday	am	- 4 miles easy run
	pm	- 6 x 800m (2 minutes 8 seconds), 400m slow jog between each repetition. Have 20 minutes rest, then run 4 x 200m quite fast, using a 200m jog for recovery
Wednesday		- 10 miles steady run
Thursday	am	- 5 miles steady run
	pm	- 7 miles run split up: 4½ miles steady, ½ mile easy, 2 miles fast
Friday		- rest day
Saturday	am	- 4 miles easy run

Saturday	pm	- use the same session as for the first 2 weeks in April but try to achieve 65 seconds at 400m pace. Also run the two fast 200m repetitions

May – middle 3 weeks

Sunday	am	- 12 miles steady run
	pm	- 8 x 150m relaxed stride – walk back recovery
Monday	am	- 5 miles easy run
	pm	- 7 miles steady run
Tuesday	am	- 4 miles easy run
	pm	- 5 x 1200m (3 minutes 15 seconds); 600m slow jog between each repetition. Have 20 minutes rest, then run 6 x 100m quite fast with 100m walk between each sprint
Wednesday		- 10 miles steady run
Thursday	am	- 5 miles easy run
	pm	- 5 miles fastish run
Friday		- rest day
Saturday	am	- 4 miles easy run
	pm	- 4 sets 5 x 400m (63/64 seconds); jog 100m between each 400m, then 400m jog between sets. After 20 minutes rest run 6 x 60m acceleration runs. Walk back recovery

May – week 4

Sunday	am	- 12 miles steady run
	pm	- 4 miles easy run
Monday	am	- 5 miles easy run
	pm	- 7 miles steady run
Tuesday	am	- 4 miles easy run

Tuesday	pm -	5 x 1200m (first 400m in 66 seconds; 2nd 400m in 62 seconds; 3rd 400m in 66 seconds). Have 800m slow jog for recovery; 20 minutes rest, then run 6 x 100m relaxed stride – walk back recovery
Wednesday	-	10 miles steady run
Thursday	am -	4 miles easy run
	pm -	6 repetitions round the hilly cross-country circuit. These should be fairly fast, but relaxed. Have 1 minute jog for recovery
Friday	-	rest day
Saturday	am -	4 miles easy run
	pm -	4 sets of 4x 500m (80 seconds); jog 100m between each 500m, then 400m jog between each set. Have 20 minutes rest then run 4 x 120m sprint. Walk back slowly between each sprint. On the 2nd week, substitute a 5000m track race for this session

Competition phase

Although in this phase, the training is intensive on some occasions, on other occasions the object is to maintain your fitness whilst saving your energy for the races.

You have to learn how to allocate effort (both mentally and physically) during the training cycle, so that each race is approached with a relaxed body and a confident mind. This phase lasts approximately 15 weeks, so I have suggested a 3-week cycle of training between important races.

First and second 3-week cycles

Week 1		
Sunday	am -	12 miles easy run
	pm -	3 miles easy run
Monday	am -	5 miles easy run
	pm -	7 miles steady run
Tuesday	am -	4 miles easy run
	pm -	5 x 1200m – run similarly to the session in the last week in May. Have 600m slow jog for recovery. After 20 minutes rest, run 6 x 60m relaxed stride: walk back recovery
Wednesday	-	10 miles steady run
Thursday	am -	5 miles easy run
	pm -	6 repetitions round the hilly 1000/1200m circuit; 30 seconds rest between each repetition
Friday	-	5 miles easy run
Saturday	am -	4 miles easy run
	pm -	5 sets 3 x 400m: No. 1 – 64 seconds; No. 2 – 64 seconds; No. 3 – 60 seconds. Have 100m jog between each 400m repetition, then 400m jog between sets

Week 2		
Sunday	am -	12 miles steady run
	pm -	8 x 100m relaxed stride – walk back recovery
Monday	am -	5 miles easy run
	pm -	5 miles fastish run

Tuesday	am	- 4 miles easy run
	pm	- 5 x 800m (2 minutes 6 seconds); 600m jog between each repetition
Wednesday		- 10 miles steady run
Thursday	am	- 4 miles easy run
	pm	- 4 x 400m (61/62 seconds); 400m jog for recovery; 4 x 200m (28/29 seconds); 200m jog for recovery
Friday		- rest day
Saturday		- 3000 race

Week 3

Sunday	am	- 10 miles steady run
	pm	- 4 miles easy run
Monday	am	- 5 miles easy run
	pm	- 6 miles steady run
Tuesday	am	- 4 miles easy run
	pm	- 2 x 1500m (3 minutes 50 seconds); 8 minutes rest between repetitions; 20 minutes rest, then run 4 x 200m fast but relaxed – s200m jog for recovery
Wednesday	am	- 10 miles easy run
	pm	- 4 miles easy run
Thursday	am	- 4 miles easy run
	pm	- 5 miles easy run
Friday		- rest day
Saturday		- 10,000m race

Third and fourth 3-week cycles

Week 1

Sunday	am	- 5 miles easy run
	pm	- 5 miles steady run
Monday		- 10 miles steady run
Tuesday	am	- 4 miles easy run
	pm	- 12 x 300m (47/48 seconds); 300m jog for recovery

Wednesday		- 10 miles steady run
Thursday	am	- 4 miles easy run
	pm	- 6 x 1000/1200m flat cross-country circuit. Run relaxed, using only 30 seconds for recovery
Friday		- 4 miles easy run
Saturday	am	- 4 miles easy run
	pm	- 5 x 1200m (1st 400m in 64 seconds; 2nd 400m in 60 seconds; 3rd 400m in 64 seconds); 2 laps jog between each repetition. After 20 minutes rest, run 6 x 60m fast relaxed strides – walk back recovery

Week 2

Sunday	am	- 12 miles easy run
	pm	- 4 miles easy run
Monday		- 10 miles steady run
Tuesday	am	- 4 miles easy run
	pm	- 8 x 500m (1st 400m in 63 seconds, then 100m fast); 400m jog between each repetition
Wednesday		- 8 miles easy run
Thursday	am	- 4 miles easy run
	pm	- 2 x 1000m (2 minutes 40 seconds); 2 laps jog for recovery. After 20 minutes rest, run 6 x 60m relaxed stride: walk back recovery
Friday		- rest day
Saturday		- 1500m race

Week 3

Sunday	am	- 10 miles easy run
	pm	- 4 miles easy run
Monday		- 10 miles steady run
Tuesday	am	- 4 miles easy run

Tuesday	pm	- 8 x 400m (62 seconds); 400m jog between each repetition
Wednesday		- 8 miles easy run
Thursday	am	- 4 miles easy run
	pm	- 8 x 200m relaxed on grass; 200m jog for recovery
Friday		- rest day
Saturday		- 5000m race

Fifth 3-week cycle

Week 1

Sunday	am	- 6 miles easy run
	pm	- 5 miles easy run
Monday		- 10 miles steady run
Tuesday	am	- 5 miles easy run
	pm	- 6 x 1000/1200m flat cross-country circuit. Run these fairly fast with 1 minute recovery between each repetition
Wednesday		- 12 miles easy run
Thursday	am	- 5 miles easy run
	pm	- 6 x 600m (1st 400m in 63 seconds, then 200m fast); 600m recovery jog between each repetition
Friday		- 6 miles easy run
Saturday	am	- 4 miles easy run
	pm	- 5 x 1200m – run these similarly to the same session in Week 1 of the previous cycle. 20 minutes rest, then 6 x 60m relaxed stride: walk back

Week 2

Sunday	am	- 12 miles easy run
	pm	- 4 miles easy run
Monday	am	- 5 miles easy run
	pm	- 4 miles fastish run
Tuesday	am	- 5 miles easy run
	pm	- 3 sets 5 x 400m (62 seconds); 200m jog between each 400m; 400m jog between sets. 20 minutes rest, then run 6 x 60m sprint. Walk back recovery
Wednesday		- 8 miles steady run
Thursday	am	- 4 miles easy run
	pm	- 8 x 200m fast relaxed strides on grass; 200m jog for recovery
Friday		- rest day
Saturday		- 3000 race

Week 3

Sunday	am	- 10 miles easy run
	pm	- 6 x 100m fastish run: walk back recovery
Monday		- 8 miles easy run
Tuesday	am	- 5 miles easy run
	pm	- 8 x 400m fairly fast but relaxed; 300m jog for recovery
Wednesday	am	- 6 miles steady run
	pm	- 10 miles steady run
Thursday		- 6 miles easy run
Friday		- rest day
Saturday		- 5000m or 10,000m race

The role of the coach

by Bruce Tulloh

The coach is the custodian of the runner's dreams. Unless the athlete and the coach can share those dreams, the coach is not really doing his job. At the heart of the coach-athlete relationship, and far more important than technical skill or competitive experience, lies the need for mutual trust and understanding. The coach cannot give the athlete what he wants unless he knows what is wanted, even when the athlete himself is not sure what he is looking for.

A few weeks before writing this chapter, I was at a meeting of some of Britain's most successful distance runners, all men who had won gold medals or broken world records. One of the group, Steve Cram, asked us all to name one major mistake we had made in our careers. Everyone there was able to confess to having made wrong decisions – over-racing, coming back too soon after injury or taking on too many commitments – decisions that we felt, with hindsight, had adversely affected performances, but which could have been better made with the help of a good second opinion. If experienced athletes at the very highest level appreciate the need for a good coach, how much more is a coach essential for the runner starting out on his career. Listening to the voice of experience helps the runner to avoid making a lot of obvious mistakes or, at least, it helps him to recognise the mistakes at an early stage. Alan Storey, who as National Marathon Coach has advised many of our top runners, including the ultra-consistent Hugh Jones, always says that he is a good coach because he made every mistake that could be made by the age of 23!

Before we consider how to find the right coach, we must look at the different kinds of coach and the different types of coach/athlete relationship, for these are many, covering the whole spectrum, from that of a teacher with a class of fifty to that of a one-to one relationship as permanent as the one between Woody Allen and his psychiatrist.

The coach of young athletes

Most coaching arrangements will start at a school or in an athletics club, where someone has been appointed to take charge of the youngsters. In most cases the person will have some form of qualification,

105

perhaps a Phys.Ed. degree or a B.A.F. coaches' award or at least many years of experience in the sport, but there is always the possibility that he is doing the job because there is no one else available. Whatever his or her background, there is no guarantee that he or she is actually the right person for this particular job.

Parents are sometimes too quick to assume that they can hand over their child to a club coach with complete confidence, because they often have a misplaced idea of what an athletics club is. Athletic clubs are not like professional football clubs. They are usually little self-help groups of enthusiasts, with no backing except the money they can raise from raffles and subscriptions. If they are lucky they have a municipal track and the use of some sort of clubhouse. The club is kept going by a handful of enthusiasts whose hobby it is, and they give hours of their time for nothing. There is seldom any money to pay for a coach so they rely on volunteers, usually parents of young athletes or older members of the club who want to put something back into it. A bad club coach may have the 'sergeant-major' approach: 'show them who's boss and make them work hard'. This may be good for the club in the short term, if the coach can bully young athletes into training hard and performing well while they are still young enough to be ordered about, but many of those athletes are likely to be lost when they get older.

The good coach, like the good teacher, has a caring, parental attitude towards his group of athletes. He or she knows that they are still developing, both mentally and physically, and that it is his job to help that development along at a pace that is right for each child. He knows that many of his charges will not stay in the sport, because they will be trying out all sorts of different pastimes in their formative years, so he must try to fill each season with positive experiences. A child develops by facing challenges and rising to overcome them; if he is allowed to duck challenges he will never mature fully, but, equally, if the challenge is too tough and he fails miserably, he may lose confidence. The secret of good coaching at this age is to give each athlete the right sort of goals, ones that can be achieved, recognised and rewarded, thereby creating the desire to go on.

Should parents coach their own children? We can all point to terrible examples of the 'pushy parent', projecting his own desire for fame onto the child, but in a club children may well be exposed to an equally ambitious coach who lacks the parents' detailed knowledge, not to mention their personal commitment. There are many examples of successful partnerships, of which Sebastian and Peter Coe are the most renowned, but there is always the danger of developing an intense atmosphere from which there is no escape. With a coach who does not live in the same house there is always a chance for tensions to be dispelled when emotions are flowing strongly. Moreover the coach can occasionally make the necessary blunt remark – perhaps to dispel an illusion or sort out a problem which it would be very difficult for a parent to make.

This brings me to another role that the coach always plays, but which is most important in the early years – that of a buffer between the athlete and the cruel world outside. By the very nature of the sport, athletes tend to be self-centred and sometimes selfish as well. At a hint of criticism from someone in the club, or perhaps merely a lack of the recognition they feel they deserve, they can go into a huff, or form a clique, or decide that they are not being appreciated. The experienced coach, who has seen it all before, can recognise that mild paranoia is common, even normal, amongst ambitious young people, and can make allowances. He needs to have the balance and the sense of humour to keep their feet on the ground even when their ambitions are gigantic. Paradoxically, his greatest problems can arise when the athlete is enjoying success. When the athlete is struggling to succeed and frequently losing, all the coach has to do is to support him, dust him off and encourage him to try again, but if the athlete is successful at a very early stage he may get an exaggerated idea of his own talent and become unwilling to accept advice.

It will already be apparent that the coach's role is far more than that of an instructor, but for young athletes in particular this is his main function: to teach techniques and devise training schedules; and to decide what the workload and the competition schedule should be. How much is enough? How much is too much? These are the questions that all athletes and coaches try to answer, and there is no single correct answer, but the coach of young athletes cannot afford to get them wrong, or he will be in trouble. When a young athlete joins a coaching group, it is advisable for the parents to find out what the coach's reputation is in this respect. I have known coaches of a teenage group who started with forty enthusiastic kids and finished up with one international and thirty-something drop-outs. That is not good coaching; it is slave-driving. The important thing is that the coach regards his athletes not as cannon-fodder for his own battle against other coaches, but as young people who must be developed, at their own pace, over several years, and who are regarded as people first and athletes second.

The years of transition

At the age of seventeen or eighteen, young people are starting out on the next phase of their lives, leaving school, starting work or going into higher education. In many cases this means leaving home and their regular circle of school friends to form new friendships. For the athlete it may mean joining a different training group, with different coaches.

Those going to a college will probably find that there are coaches there who have a different approach to the sport. Both the athlete and the coach have to make considerable adjustments at this stage. The

coach is not taking on a child who will automatically follow his dictat, nor is he taking on a mature athlete who has firm ideas about his goals. The 'student' athlete, and I shall use this term to apply to those between the ages of seventeen and twenty-one, is in a state of flux in more ways than one. Not only is he or she moving from dependence to independence and adjusting his or her views of what is important in life, but physical maturation is being reached. The brilliant school athlete may be being overtaken by the late developers. This is fine for the late developers, who have always been struggling in the past and so are used to hard work, but it demands a re-appraisal of attitude from the talented athlete who has been able to win

A good club coach develops a working relationship with his athletes. These runners are doing a speedwork session on the track under their coach's supervision.

without a lot of preparation, but who now finds that life is much tougher.

At this stage, the forming of a coach-athlete relationship is very much a lottery. The university or college coach seldom knows who is going to turn up in the freshmen squad, and there is no guarantee that the athlete is going to see eye to eye with the coach. Since the college athlete is only there for three years, with one third of the squad changing every year, there is not time to build up the close supportive relationship which I feel is essential for success at the highest level.

However, this loss is not without certain benefits. Firstly, the athlete must make his own decision about whether he wants to take the sport seriously. Once he has made this conscious decision, without being pressurized by club or parents, he is much more likely to continue with the sport in later years. Secondly, the college coach has a tremendous amount of experience, because he sees so many athletes, of different levels of talent, pass through his hands. A college coach with a squad of thirty will handle a hundred athletes in ten years, whereas a club coach might see half that number in that time. The college coach will usually offer a wide variety of different types of group training weights, circuits, gym work, speed training on the track, hill running and endurance work off the track. With a large menu to choose from and a variety of people to train with, as well as competition at the right level, the college athlete is well provided for, even though the personal touch may be lacking.

The author Bruce Tulloh is shown here in training with Richard Nerurkar, the 1993 British Cross-country Champion and the World Cup Marathon Champion, whom he coaches.

Coaching the mature athlete

One of my international colleagues once said to me, "Of course, nothing that you do before the age of twenty-one matters." I did not agree, but I took his point, that all competition in the junior years can be regarded as merely the launching pad for the career of the senior athlete. It is at this stage that it is important to find the right coach, and it is unlikely to be the person who was coaching the same athlete at the age of fourteen. The club-level athlete needs a club-level coach and the ambitious athlete needs an ambitious coach, or at least one who can identify with his ambitions. The matter is too important to be left to chance. If the athlete feels that the right coach does not exist in his club, he should consider either changing clubs or going to some national coach for advice.

The establishment of a relationship must start with a 'courtship' in which the two parties get to know each other, and

109

Most club coaches meet their athletes at the track two or three times a week and he works out their personal training plans on a weekly basis. He can help to plan their racing plans, season by season, so that they peak at the right times.

during which certain questions need to be asked, even if they are not posed directly. Let us assume that the athlete has just finished his education and has started a new job in a large town, with several clubs and coaching groups in the area. He has already reached a high national level in his age group and he has ambitions of an international career. The implication of this is that if his athletic career is really successful he will be able to become a full-time athlete. He is recommended by a friend to join a certain coach. What questions should the athlete ask the coach? I suggest that he needs to find out the answers to the following:

● How many years have you been in coaching?

● What are your qualifications for being a coach?

● What is your own competitive experience?

● How many athletes have you coached to national or international level?

● How much do you know about the training being done by the world's best athletes in my event?

● How much time are you prepared to give me?

Of these questions, the last is the most important, but it cannot be answered until the coach knows what kind of athlete he is dealing with. The questions to which the coach will want to know the answers go as follows:

● What is your best performance in your main event?

● What is your best performance in the past season?

● Are you convinced that this is going to remain your main event, or have you other ambitions?

● For how many years have you been running seriously ?

● What injuries have you had?

● What commitments have you outside your sport?

● What are your ultimate ambitions?

● How much time are you prepared to put in to reach your goal?

Of these questions, the last two are the most important.

The unwritten contract

Once the athlete and the coach have agreed to work together on a trial basis they become parties to an unwritten contract. I am talking here about proper coaching, where the coach and athlete meet at least once a week and probably more. Advice by letter is just advice, not really coaching.

In this contract, the runner says to the coach: *"I will agree to stick as closely as I can to the training on which we have agreed, whatever anyone else is doing."*

"I will not consult any other coach or athlete for advice without telling you first."

"I will not enter races without discussing the programme with you beforehand."

"I will agree to follow your guidance for twelve months, to see how it works out."

The coach is saying to the runner:
"I agree to put all my knowledge at your disposal, but I will not dictate what your training will be – that is a matter for discussion."

"Once we have agreed on a training programme. I expect you to carry it through."

"I would like to be part of your decision-making, when planning your athletic career over several years."

"As far as is possible, I will be there whenever you need me."

"You can rely on me as much when you are doing badly as when you are doing well."

Financial considerations

Athletics has always been a poor man's sport, and the tradition has always been that the coach has passed on his expertise to fellow athletes without charge. This is in direct contrast to sports such as tennis, where most coaches charge by the hour, thus restricting the sport to those fortunate children whose parents can afford to pay for their coaching.

However, the money that has come into the sport since the early 1980s *has*

changed things; the athlete who is at the top of the British list and in the world's top twenty can probably expect an annual income of $1,000,000. The best may pay their coach a retaining fee, but others with a smaller income cannot support a personal coach full-time, but will pay the coach's way to training camps and major championships and to cover his expenses around the country.

To the average club coach, however, this is just pie in the sky. He is certainly not doing it for the money, but there are ways in

111

Many athletes find it beneficial to train together as a squad, especially on long weekend runs. Their coach will plan the different phases of their training on an individual basis according to their level of fitness and personal racing plans.

which coaching could become at least a part-time job and possibly lead to a career. In some countries, where there are fewer clubs receiving money from the Federation, the coach is paid a part-time salary by the club. In return for this he attends the track at certain regular times and comes to major fixtures. Another way is to regard the coach as a kind of social services worker who is employed to work at a municipal track, just as the council employs librarians to work in the local library.

There are salaried national coaches who work for the British Athletics Federation, whose role is development of coaches and coaching through the BAF Coach Education and related programmes; and development of athletes through club, regional and national programmes. National coaches also coach individual athletes, but as honorary coaches in their own time. There are also National Event coaches, who receive some money from the Federation but derive their main income from other jobs. In the United States, there are hundreds of salaried coaches, but most of these are only employed by universities to coach the athletes of that college for inter-collegiate competition. There are no professional athletics coaches employed at British universities or colleges. As long as 95 per cent of the athletes in the UK remain amateur, both in spirit and in reality, the financial returns from coaching are going to vary from small to non-existent. The rewards that come from successful coaching are measured in club victories, personal bests, gold medals (occasionally) and life-long friendships.

The complete coach

As athlete and coach get to know each other, they will work out their own pattern of operating. The commonest arrangement is to meet at the track one or two evenings a week plus one morning over the weekend, and for plans to be worked out on a week to week basis. The coach might be seeing ten or a dozen athletes on a regular basis, as well as handling the problems of an equal number who turn up at irregular intervals, usually when something has gone wrong. This is how most operate, but in my opinion this does not go nearly far enough.

The essential thing in raising an athlete to a new level of performance is regular monitoring, and that means seeing or talking to the athlete every day. As the runner gets nearer and nearer to the top, the old questions: "How much is enough?" and "How much is too much?" become paramount. They *can* be answered, if the coach is watching and measuring the athlete very closely over a number of years, and if the athlete is keeping a detailed training diary, but the answers only apply to that athlete for that year, and in the following year the situation must be re-appraised.

The coach of a really successful athlete becomes not so much an instructor, although he will still plan the schedules, as the head of a team, as in motor racing. The nearer the athlete gets to his physical limits in training, the more he needs the attention of a good masseur and a good physio. In Victorian times, the masseurs became the first coaches, and massage was inseparable from coaching. It is only in this decade that the value of regular massage for athletes has been appreciated. The coach is advised to go on a sports massage course himself or to get someone else to do it for him, but he will still need to use the services of a physiotherapist, to inspect the athlete regularly and spot injuries before they become serious. The coach will also need to have on hand the services of a dietitian and a chiropodist (for long-distance runners only). He would be well advised to use the services of a sports psychologist, unless he knows the athlete so well that he feels this to be unnecessary. Lastly, he needs to be on good terms with the athlete's agent and international team manager – partly to arrange the racing programme harmoniously and partly because if he doesn't get on with these people he stands little chance of getting into the stadium to see his athlete run in a major Games!

There are cases where the athlete's agent is also his coach. This, I feel, is a disastrous confusion of roles. The agent will be representing more than one athlete, I know, but the agent's chief motivation is to get his athletes winning races so that they bring money in. The coach's chief motivation is to have his athlete win a national or an international title. There will thus come a time, say when the athlete is coming back after injury, when the sensible precaution would be not to race until the training and the time-trials

have given the 'all-clear'. The coach would say: "Don't race until you are ready", but the agent, tempted by a fat appearance fee, might say: "Go on, give it a go", on the basis of one decent training session.

The most important role of the coach, once the athlete has reached physical maturity, is as a second opinion, a sounding board for the athlete's plans. The opportunities for competition are now so numerous at every level that the athlete must have a definite racing plan, season by season. Once this is established, the different phases of training can be planned – where to put in the strength work or the altitude training, when to begin the hardest training phase and when to taper off.

The climactic point for the serious athlete is going to be his performance in

Every successful athlete works hand-in-hand with his coach to achieve results. Here Ingrid Kristiansen is shown training near Oslo in Norway.

the national championships or in an international meeting. There will be only a few races each year that really count. The art of the coach lies in getting his athlete to a peak of fitness for those crucial days. Of course, it helps if he knows about the physiology of training and the psychology of competition, but the thing he needs to know most about is his athlete and the way he responds to different workloads. This can only be found by trial and error – and the keeping of detailed diaries – over many years. Continuity is vital. The most important role of the coach is as confidant and friend, sharing the same dreams, working towards the same goal.

The physiology of fitness

by Yiannis (John) Koutedakis

It is widely known that the athletes of today run faster than their counterparts of the past. For example, in 1928 the 800m World records were 1:51.6 and 2:16.8 for men and women respectively compared to the record times of 1:41.73 and 1:53.28 at the time of writing. Sports physiology, nutrition, medicine and psychology have all contributed to these performance enhancements, as they are the only legitimate approaches for understanding and monitoring improvements in running.

Sports physiology is mainly used to assess *physical fitness* and to detect areas of weakness which require special attention. For running events, fitness could be defined as a composite dependent on the levels of *aerobic* (i.e., with oxygen) and *anaerobic* (i.e., without oxygen) metabolism, together with muscle *speed* and *strength*. *Muscle elasticity* and *body composition* may also be included in fitness assessments. However, no single measurement can disclose the physical fitness of runners, as fitness components vary markedly depending on the individual, the specific event, and the level of performance.

Before examining the various components of fitness for running and

their variation throughout seasons of training and competition, a brief introduction to muscle physiology, and the energy production mechanisms is helpful.

Muscle and muscle fibre characteristics

If you were to examine a whole skeletal muscle and gradually dissect it into its component parts, it would first be seen that the muscle is composed of bundles of *fibres* (see page 116). Each of these fibres is a cylindrical, elongated cell; its thickness varies in different muscles or even in the same muscle, and may be from 10 µm to 100 µm (1 µm = 1 thousandth of a millimetre). In addition to finding the normal constituents of cells, such as mitochondria (i.e. microscopic self-contained structures where oxygen is actually delivered and used), muscle cells contain specialized *contractile filaments* grouped in *sarcomeres*, together with an elaborate internal membrane system which controls contraction. These contractile filaments (by which muscle force is generated) are situated in *myofibrils* 1-2 µm in diameter running the whole length of

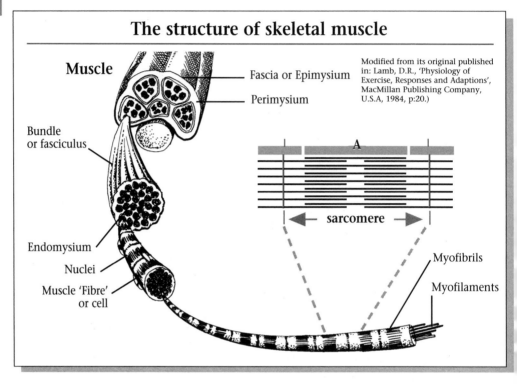

The structure of skeletal muscle

Muscle

Fascia or Epimysium

Perimysium

Modified from its original published in: Lamb, D.R., 'Physiology of Exercise, Responses and Adaptions', MacMillan Publishing Company, U.S.A, 1984, p:20.)

Bundle or fasciculus

A

← sarcomere →

Endomysium

Nuclei

Muscle 'Fibre' or cell

Myofibrils

Myofilaments

the muscle fibre and contain most of the protein of the muscle cell. The functional unit within a whole muscle is the group of muscle fibres supplied by a single motor nerve fibre: the *motor unit.*

Within each muscle fibre and at the level of the above mentioned contractile filaments, muscle contraction occurs when the cross-bridges of the thick (myosin) filaments (opposite left) bind to selected sites on the thin (actin) filaments. As a result of this selective binding, the filaments slide past one another, maintaining their original lengths but reducing the overall length of the sarcomere (opposite right). If the muscle is fully contracted, filaments may overlap and interfere with each other, with thick filaments pressing against the Z-discs, thus reducing the force a muscle can generate.

Muscle biopsy techniques (see page 118) are used to study human muscle fibre types. On the basis of their contractile characteristics, two main fibre types can be found in human muscle: type I (or slow twitch fibres), and type II (or fast twitch fibres), forming slow and fast motor-units respectively. Type II fibres are larger in diameter, rich in fibrils, surrounded by fewer blood capillaries, are low in mitochondria and myoglobin concentration (which are part of the

Thick and thin filaments

Thick filament (myosin)

Myosin crossbridges

Thin filament (actin)

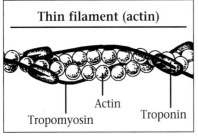

Actin

Tropomyosin

Troponin

Modified and redrawn from: Murray, J. and Weber, A. "the cooperative action of muscle proteins." *Scientific America, 1974, 230(2): 58-71*

Above: Close-up of the thin and thick filaments. The thin filament contains three different proteins: actin, troponin and tropomyosin.

Right: The sliding filament model. The thin and thick filaments slide past one another, resulting in a shortening of the overall length of the sarcomere. The sarcomere is contained between two Z-discs and it is regarded as the contractile unit within the myofibrils.

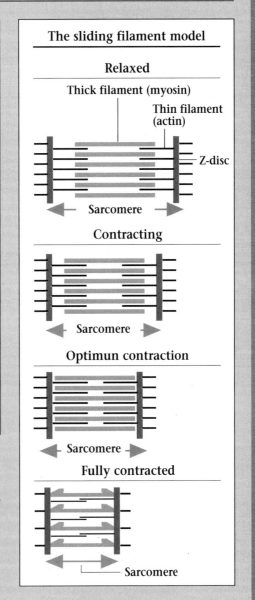

The sliding filament model

Relaxed

Thick filament (myosin)

Thin filament (actin)

Z-disc

Sarcomere

Contracting

Sarcomere

Optimun contraction

Sarcomere

Fully contracted

Sarcomere

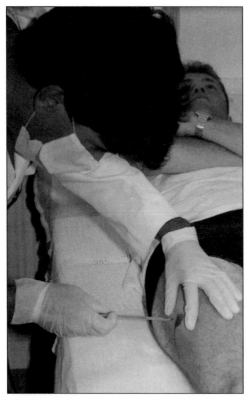

This muscle biopsy has been performed on an athlete's right vastus lateralis for subsequent determination of the muscle fibre profile.

oxygen transport system), and possess a higher capacity for anaerobic work (e.g. short, high intensity running) than the fibres classified as slow twitch. Different chemical features may also be observed in the type II fibre population leading to a further classification into types IIa and IIb (type IIa share characteristics of both fast and slow muscle fibres).

Sprinters, middle-distance and long-distance runners differ with regard to their relative proportions of type I and type II

fibres. Elite sprinters may have as high as 92 per cent type II muscle fibres, whereas elite marathon runners may demonstrate similar high percentages in type I fibres. No differences have been found in muscle fibre profiles between the two sexes and intense physical training causes no change in muscle fibre proportions by number. However, the size of different types of fibre may selectively change with appropriate training.

Energy production mechanisms

The specific energy required for thin-thick filament interaction is provided by Adenosine Triphosphate (ATP) which is merely a transport vehicle for energy. Muscle contractions would only last for approximately one second if ATP could not be resynthesized at a rate equal to that of its use. ATP resynthesis implies that energy must be obtained from muscle fuels to reform the ATP from adenosine diphosphate (ADP):

ADP + Energy from Muscle Fuel → ATP

There are three different modes of energy (ATP) production which can be derived from anaerobic and aerobic metabolic processes:

- Anaerobic Metabolism (or Anaerobic System)
  a) The ATP-CP System (this is also called the *Phosphagen System*, or *Anaerobic Alactic System*)
  b) The Lactic Acid System
- Aerobic Metabolism (or Aerobic System)

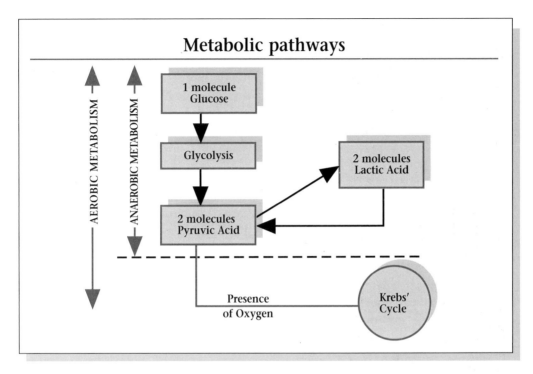

Metabolic pathways

AEROBIC METABOLISM

ANAEROBIC METABOLISM

1 molecule
Glucose

Glycolysis

2 molecules
Pyruvic Acid

2 molecules
Lactic Acid

Presence
of Oxygen

Krebs'
Cycle

When exercise begins, release of the energy from the rich chemical bonds of the phosphagens ATP and creatine phosphate (CP) enables muscle contraction to start immediately. However, on their own, these high-energy phosphagens can only cover the energy requirements for less than ten seconds of maximal effort.

As exercise continues, levels of ATP decline to some extent. Despite this, muscles do not become depleted because a reduction in ATP concentration stimulates a rapid breakdown of muscle glycogen (during a procedure called *glycolysis*) to resynthesize ATP and thus maintain an adequate energy supply for exercise.

One molecule of muscle glycogen, on its way to form two molecules of pyruvic acid, contributes two molecules of ATP. This is known as *anaerobic glycolysis* (as shown above) and it is part of anaerobic metabolism. If sufficient oxygen is available, the pyruvic acid enters Krebs' cycle within mitochondria, where a further 36 molecules of ATP may be produced aerobically during a biochemical procedure known as *aerobic glycolysis*. If, on the other hand, there is not enough oxygen as in very intense activity, pyruvic acid is transformed to lactic acid, to allow the process to go on longer. (The difference between *lactic acid* and *lactate* has a biochemical basis: lactic acid can dissociate to produce lactate and a positively charged hydrogen ion.)

The contribution of anaerobic metabolic pathways to the overall energy production of a given physical demand is relatively minor during exercise of several minutes. For exercise or running events lasting for more than two minutes, aerobic glycolysis is the main energy source and the muscle fibres predominately involved in contraction are type I. However, anaerobically generated energy could be the main limiting factor during maximal exercise lasting approximately from 10 seconds to two minutes; in this case the fibres primarily involved in muscle contraction are type II.

Aerobic fitness and its measurement

The principal limiting factors for most running events that last longer than two minutes are the ability of the heart, lungs and circulation to deliver oxygen to the working muscles, and the ability of the muscles to receive and use the oxygen. Aerobic fitness, therefore, is closely associated with a number of physical and physiological adaptations and/or characteristics, due to prolonged endurance training.

Great *cardiac size* in elite distance runners is a well known adaptation. Paavo Nurmi, for example, was found to have a heart more than double the normal size. However, no information is available regarding heart sizes of runners before they engaged in endurance training, leaving a question mark over the issue of heredity.

Cardiac size affects the blood circulation measurements of *stroke volume* and *cardiac output*. Indeed, although most distance runners possess a lower resting heart rate than age-matched untrained individuals, the volume of blood ejected from the heart with each beat (i.e. stroke volume) may be nearly double the normal volume. During maximal exercise, cardiac output of blood may increase from resting levels of about 6 litres/min to levels in excess of 25 litres/min at maximal heart rates of 190-210 beats/min.

The most dramatic evidence of adaptation to endurance training is the increased concentration of *mitochondria* and the *enzymes* responsible for energy production within muscle during aerobic muscular effort. Multiplication of mitochondria may result in the channelling of a greater proportion of the pyruvate formed by glycolysis into the mitochondrial oxidative pathway and less into lactate. Endurance training also increases the *capillary density* of human muscle. This enhances the total oxidative capacity of the muscle, primarily by reducing the distance all substances, including oxygen, have to diffuse and by providing a greater blood flow to the working muscle fibres.

The ability to consume large volumes of oxygen during exhaustive effort have been associated with the limits of human endurance and, therefore, aerobic fitness. The term *maximal oxygen intake* (VO_2 max) has been introduced to represent the greatest utilization of oxygen in a given

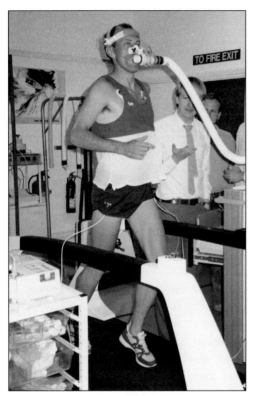

This shows Steve Ovett performing a maximal oxygen intake (VO2 max) test on a treadmill.

time during exercise (see above); research has shown that VO_2 max values can be affected by various factors such as age, sex, training state and high altitude.

While the normally active 20-year-old male has a VO_2 max of approximately 46 ml/kg/min (i.e. millilitres per kilogramme body weight per minute), trained distance runners normally demonstrate values in excess of 70 and 75 ml/kg/min for females and males respectively. A value of 92 ml/kg/min has been reported for a British male, international distance runner. In

assessing national and international runners, it is not unusual to find VO_2 max values in middle-distance runners to be higher than those obtained from their long-distance counterparts; training intensity rather than training volume may be a brief explanation for such findings. However, performance in middle and/or long distance running could not be predicted from VO_2 max levels alone.

Ventilating the lungs with air, and the intake of oxygen must keep pace with exercise to allow blood to be re-oxygenated and emptied of carbon dioxide. The total volume of air breathed in from the atmosphere per minute is referred to as *minute ventilation* (V_E). This value varies from about 15 litres/min at rest to 160-185 litres/min during maximal treadmill exercise performed by elite male long/middle-distance runners.

The anaerobic threshold (AT) has also been used for laboratory monitoring of aerobic performance. AT may be defined as the rate of work at which part of the energy requirement is just supplemented by anaerobic metabolism. High AT levels have frequently been associated with elite performance levels in middle- and long-distance running. For both research and coaching purposes, AT is normally expressed as a percentage of the VO_2 max and may be as high as 95 per cent in marathon runners. Values from 60-90 per cent have been measured in British Olympic middle-distance runners.

Blood lactate measurements have also been conducted to invasively determine AT levels in runners. In such cases, AT is defined as the running intensity at which lactate begins to accumulate in the working muscle above certain levels; approximately 2.5 and 4 mmol per litre of blood have been found to be the AT for elite and recreational male and female runners respectively.

Anaerobic fitness and its measurement

Anaerobic fitness may be defined as the ability for intense muscular contractions that require substantially greater rates of energy (ATP) production than can be provided by aerobic metabolism alone. Such muscular activity can be sustained for less than two minutes during which ATP

Factors affecting anaerobic fitness

Among the factors that may affect anaerobic fitness, and therefore intensive running performance are:

- Rates of ATP release
- Levels of muscle glycogen
- Levels of lactic acid buffers (which help to neutralise the acid)
- Rates of lactate removal
- Skeletal muscle fibre distribution (type II fibres are better equipped to perform anaerobically)
- Tolerance to high acid levels (measured in pH units) due to increased lactate accumulation

turnover may increase by approximately 1000-fold. In a sprinting man, for example, the rate of ATP turnover is approximately 2.7 mmol/sec/kg of body mass.

As we have already shown, regeneration of ATP by the phosphagen system does not result in lactate formation and is known as *alactic*. On the other hand, ATP production through anaerobic glycolysis does result in lactic acid formation and thus is termed *lactic*. Therefore, anaerobic fitness depends on both the alactic and lactic systems' ability to generate ATP.

Sport scientists feel that performance, expressed as fatigue resistance during maximal muscular effort, mainly depends on the degree of lactate buffering and dispersal, as well as to a number of aspects related to high lactate levels. Indeed, elevated lactate levels could ultimately decrease body acidity to levels too low for glycolysis to continue.

While the measurement, for example, of oxygen intake levels is a highly reliable way to assess aerobic fitness, no such widely accepted methods are available for anaerobic fitness evaluations. However, measurements of peak *lactic acid* levels and the application of the *Wingate Anaerobic Test* (WAT) can provide both runners and coaches with useful information for training.

As a result of any type of exercise, net lactic acid output reflects the balance of lactate production and removal in the muscle cell. Lactic acid is formed as a result of:

1 High energy (ATP) demand

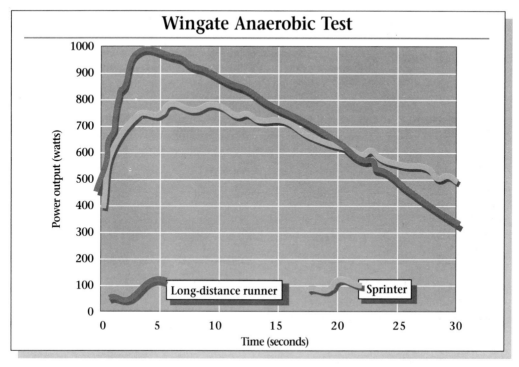

Wingate Anaerobic Test

Power output (watts) vs Time (seconds)

Long-distance runner

Sprinter

2 Insufficient supply of oxygen

3 Rapid fluctuations of energy demand

When the body is in a transition state (e.g. continuous running where speed is evaluated every one, two, or three minutes) the balance favours net lactic acid production and lactate rises within the muscle cells.

Peak lactic acid levels are normally lower when a steady-state level is reached following 10-20 minutes of continuous work, even if running speeds correspond to very high percentages of VO_2 max. However, following short but intensive running, maximal lactate concentrations of approximately 9 and 17 mmol per litre of blood can be obtained from endurance

The Wingate Anaerobic Test: power output for a male international long-distance runner and for a male elite sprinter.

runners and sprinters respectively.

The WAT, is relatively easy to administer and has been used for testing anaerobic power of both arms and legs. It involves all-out cycle ergometer work for approximately 30 seconds against a resistance usually based on body mass. Following 30 seconds of all-out work, a 25 per cent decrease in muscle glycogen, a 66 per cent decrease in creatine phosphate, and an 82 per cent increase in blood lactate concentration may be observed in trained runners.

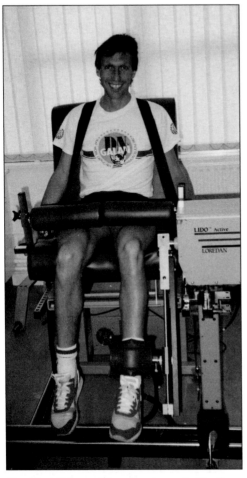

Here David Moorcroft is performing an isokinetic strength test with his left leg.

It has also been calculated that approximately 30 per cent of the ATP necessary to perform a 30-second all-out test comes from anaerobic alactic and about 64 per cent from anaerobic glycolytic pathways. Computerized versions of the WAT may provide information regarding the runner's peak

power and mean power outputs, time required to reach peak power, and a fatigue index. Furthermore, variation between events and individuals may be reflected by different shaped 'power curves' (see page 123).

The influence of training on the anaerobic fitness of skeletal muscle is not as clear as that relating to aerobic fitness. Short duration high intensity training may result in increased levels of phosphagens in humans. However, the observed small changes in ATP concentration following anaerobic training may also be due to higher mitochondrial density in trained muscles, rather than an adaptation to this type of work. A few studies have also demonstrated increased muscle glycogen concentration, increased ability to buffer the lactic acid, and increased removal rates of lactic acid from the blood in anaerobically trained subjects compared to their controls.

Muscle strength and its measurement

Strength is the ability of a runner to overcome external resistance or to counter external forces, by contracting his/her muscle. This is the result of the unique characteristic of the muscle cell, whereby it can convert the chemical energy of ATP into mechanical work. The important functional property of muscle therefore, is its ability to create *tension* and therefore to generate *force*. *Maximal strength, speed-strength* and *strength-endurance* are the most commonly used classifications of strength in sport.

Muscle area, muscle quality, type of contraction, muscle co-ordination and synchronisation are among the factors affecting strength performance. The two latter factors are often regarded as synonymous with sport skills and are thought to primarily involve a 'neural' function, such as the recruitment of muscle fibres. The contribution of this neural component may be more important in the early stages of a strength-training programme, and may account for up to 20 per cent in strength gains with little or no *hypertrophy* (as the enlargement of muscle is called). In other words, muscle hypertrophy is not a necessary consequence of increasing strength. However, as training volumes continue to increase, then hypertrophy becomes more dominant.

Muscle hypertrophy is closely related to strength gains following heavy resistance strength training programmes undertaken for more than three months. Hypertrophy results mainly from the enlargement of fibres due to an increased number of myofibrils, especially in type II muscle fibres. Hypertrophy is normally measured as the total muscle cross-sectional area. However, after correction for muscle cross-sectional area, there seems to be little difference between untrained individuals of dissimilar ages and sex regarding muscle strength. The average tension of untrained human muscle has been found to be approximately three kg per square cm.

Simple mechanical dynamometers, strain gauges, and computerised equipment with accommodating speed and resistance facilities have been used to obtain data regarding the tension developed by various muscle groups in male and female competitors, including runners. It has been established for example, that hand-grip strength is a reasonably valid indicator of strength status of almost the entire body musculature; high levels of hand-grip strength are normally accompanied with high strengths of different muscle groups such as back and thigh.

Muscle strength assessments on isokinetic machines (see page 124) at relatively low velocities of movement have revealed, not surprisingly, that elite sprinters are stronger than their long-distance counterparts. For example, male long-distance runners may demonstrate peak muscle torque levels of around 220 and 120 Newton metres (N.m) for quadriceps and hamstrings respectively. The equivalent values for female distance runners are approximately 160 and 85 N.m. On the other hand, male and female sprinters demonstrate values in excess of 330 and 220 N.m. for their quadriceps, and 160 and 110 N.m. for their hamstrings respectively. These figures illustrate that all runners need strength to varying degrees, depending on the demands of their event.

Levels of strength together with muscle strength balance (e.g. between knee flexors and extensors) are generally recognised as major components for injury prevention and for successful participation, particularly, in the shorter explosive sprinting distances. Indeed, isokinetic dynamometry has shown that hamstring to quadriceps peak muscle force ratios of less than 50 per cent can be associated with low-back pain and/or discomfort in different competitors, including runners. To resolve such complications, appropriate weight training should be used in combination with endurance, flexibility and/or skill activities in programmes designed to improve running conditioning.

Muscle elasticity – plyometrics

For the last two decades it has been believed that the elastic properties of muscle and tendon play an important role in human movement. Physiologists are in favour of the theory that the elastic components of muscle play a role which is more or less comparable to the performance of a spring.

Furthermore, the cross-bridge heads of the myosin filaments are rotated backwards, during muscle stretch, against their natural tendency to a position of higher potential energy. This could provide storage of mechanical energy within the actin-myosin cross-bridges, which in turn can be re-used during the subsequent positive work, if the muscle is allowed to shorten immediately after the stretch. This is known as the muscle 'stretch-shortening cycle' and is a dominant feature in a great number of movements in sport (e.g. the stretching-shortening cycle of the thigh antagonist muscles during sprint running).

These ideas have led many athletes and coaches to apply the principles of the stretch-shortening contraction cycle in the form of specific exercises termed *plyometrics* (e.g. various vertical and long jumps followed by explosive rebounds). The aim of plyometrics is to provide an optimum relationship between strength and speed, which will ultimately result in gains in *explosive power*.

Body composition

Somatotyping
This is a technique frequently used to compare performers competing in different events and to classify them according to body dimensions and characteristics. This is simply a means of describing the degree of roundness (endomorphy), muscularity (mesomorphy), and linearity (ectomorphy) of the body. Although somatotyping is of little practical value to the running coach, research has shown that elite male and female long/middle-distance runners are predominately ectomorphic individuals, while sprinters tend to be mesomorphs.

Percentage body fat – lean body mass
Body weight may be divided into two components: *body fat*, and the rest, which is known as the *lean body mass* or *fat free mass*. In recent years, body fat assessments have replaced the simpler weight for height measures as a more accurate way of comparing the body composition of different competitors, including runners.

Fat is stored in adipocytes (i.e. fat cells), located generally under the skin,

Average percentages of body fat (BF)

Sport	Sex	Age	Weight (kg)	BF (%)
Gymnasts	female	15.2	45.3	13.4
Wrestlers	male	19.6	74.8	8.8
Mid dist runners	male	25.7	62.9	7.3
Mid dist runners	female	24.1	52.8	14.8
Sprinters	female	21.6	60.7	18.1
Sprinters	male	23.4	82.3	9.1
Ice dancers	female	19.3	52.1	22.0
Squash	female	18.4	62.1	24.7
Hockey	male	27.8	75.6	12.3
Road cyclists	male	20.0	68.9	8.7
Lightweight rowers	male	24.3	70.3	6.7
Rugby	male	20.6	64.4	21.0
Judo	male	21.8	72.2	16.0
Nordic skiers	male	25.8	73.6	8.2

body fat weight is reflected in body density. Thus, body density decreases as the body fat proportion increases. This is good for, say, long-distance swimming, but bad for most other sport activities.

Very few studies conducted on athletic populations have reported body fat values less than 5 per cent of total body mass, indicating that a certain minimal level of fat is necessary. Indeed, very low levels of fat may result in abnormal biological functioning and, perhaps in decreased running performance.

Sports *amenorrhoea* (i.e. absence of periods), is one such abnormal biological function which coaches and women runners should bear in mind. This condition is associated with low levels of the female hormone *oestrogen*, which helps to control bone calcium; low oestrogen may cause *osteoporosis* (i.e. calcium and bone mineral loss) which increases the likelihood of stress fractures. Elite women middle/long-distance runners and ballet dancers are prime candidates for developing osteoporosis of varying severity.

Body fat values of between 6 to 11 per cent and 13 to 18 per cent of body mass could be considered as acceptable levels for elite male and female runners respectively. However, variability in body fat between competitors participating in the same running sport could occur for several reasons: it could reflect natural variation in patterns of fat distribution or could be related to individual eating and exercise patterns. It is therefore advisable to avoid establishing a specific per cent body fat

especially at the back of the arms and on the hips, thighs and bust in women, and in the abdomen in men. Quantitative determination of stored body fat is defined by the number and size of the adipocytes.

Muscle tissue constitutes the main variable of fat free mass, and consists of 19.4 per cent protein, 73.8 per cent water, and 6.8 per cent minerals, whereas adipose tissue contains 90 per cent fat and 10 per cent water. As muscle is denser than fat, the relative proportion of fat free mass to for competitors of a given sport, as important intra-individual characteristics could be neglected.

Body weight control

In elite, lean individuals, a relatively short period of six to eight weeks of dietary restriction, carried out during normal physical training and leading to six to seven per cent body weight loss, may be associated with significant reductions in certain fitness components, such as anaerobic threshold and leg muscle force levels. Under these circumstances, approximately 50 per cent of the body weight loss may be of lean tissue (i.e. muscle), which is higher than the 22 per cent suggested by Webster and other researchers to be an optimal figure for muscle loss during attempts to control weight, and contrary to the common belief that exercise prevents lean tissue loss at the expense of fat.

However, more prolonged, gradual periods of body weight regulation have no or little effect on important fitness components despite the fact that similar values of body weight and lean tissue to those described above may be obtained. It is possible that the longer weight-reduction period provides more time for appropriate biochemical and mechanical adaptations. It is suggested that athletes who are required to reach a specific body weight should be encouraged to prevent excessive weight increase in the first place, and to ensure that any excess weight be gradually reduced over at least four months.

Seasonal variations of fitness components

Training for successful competition at national and international level in many sports has become an almost year-round endeavour. Many athletics coaches have divided training and competition years into such phases as *off/in-season*, *pre/post-season*, and *pre/post-competition* periods, to mention just a few of the terms in common use. The consensus of most authorities is that optimal training can enable competitors to more efficiently utilise their musculoskeletal and cardiorespiratory systems, improve aspects related to body composition, muscle flexibility and joint mobility, and reduce the rate of sports injuries.

Several studies have examined the effects of periods of competition, training, detraining or reduced training on aspects of fitness, including endurance, strength and speed. Depending on levels of performance, the reported swings in fitness parameters may be as high as 15 per cent from one season to another. However, such swings do not occur at the same time of the year. In general, anaerobic components of fitness remain relatively unchanged throughout the competitive phases of the year, while aerobic metabolism and muscular strength may demonstrate noticeable changes.

Periods of detraining may also lead to changes in components of physical fitness. For instance, a three-month detraining period has demonstrated an approximate

15 per cent decrease in VO_2 max in young female middle-distance runners, compared to VO_2 max values obtained at the end of a competition season (12).

Aerobic power and strength in elite runners

Reduced VO_2 max and muscle strength measurements have been obtained from runners and other elite competitors at the final stages of a competitive season. Given that aerobic power during activities lasting over two minutes contributes to sporting success, declines in VO_2 max levels may result in impaired competition performance. Similarly, unfavourable qualitative and quantitative variations in muscular strength and power are likely to impair running performance given the need for requisite muscle force levels for success, especially in events involving rapid whole body acceleration.

Some authorities attribute these decrements to long-term fatigue. Others contend that the genetically determined individual maximal limits associated to aerobic power and muscular strength have long been reached in most elite runners; therefore, certain periodical declines in these measurements is not a surprising phenomenon.

Aerobic power and strength in trained runners

A slightly different picture to the one described above may be obtained from runners with an adequately developed aerobic metabolism, but not of elite

standard. At the final stages of an athletics season of training and competition, trained runners may show no or very few variations in aspects associated with aerobic performance, in line with data referring to other sports. Inappropriate training and training planning, rather than the development of efficient respiratory systems through practice and competition, may be a tentative explanation for such findings.

Regarding strength, a competitive season provides inadequate stimuli for muscle force enhancement in trained runners. In fact, available literature confirms that the ability to maintain muscular strength decreases during a competition season, despite uninterrupted continuation of event-specific training.

Given that during competitive seasons trained runners (and especially their long-distance counterparts) traditionally tend to undertake no strength sessions, one could safely assume that track-based training alone may not necessarily lead to further strength improvements, or even strength maintenance, in runners with reasonable levels of muscle strength. It may also be that, as in the case of other fitness parameters, muscle strength must complete a biological cycle of 'peaks' and 'troughs' despite attempts by coaches and conditioning experts to do otherwise.

Aerobic power and strength in novice runners

Seasons of training may lead to considerable functional improvements of the cardiorespiratory system, coupled with measurable increases in muscular strength, in male and female novice runners. Relatively low initial levels of fitness at the beginning of their training programmes could be an explanation for such observations. It should be added here that improvements of the cardiorespiratory system, muscle strength, and aspects of anaerobic metabolism may also be seen in children and adolescents engaged in sports.

Body fat and heart rates

A number of reports based on comparisons of pre-season and post-season data have indicated that in-season training and competition programmes do not elicit changes in body fat (express as percentages of body weight) in well conditioned runners. Low initial body fat levels have been the main reason given for this lack of change, during a season of very high physical activity. This may be supported by the findings of Glick and Kaufman who reported that changes in body fat and, therefore, body weight are related to initial level of skinfold thickness rather than to the effect of training; the higher the competition level the smaller the body fat changes that can be observed at the end of a competitive season, compared to its start. On the other hand, in-season periods may demonstrate significant body fat decreases in novice male and female runners.

Lastly, resting and exercise heart rates are not generally affected by periods of training and competition, in healthy and trained individuals. However, periodical evaluations in resting heart rate and heart rate during exercise have been observed among well-trained individuals, including runners; it has been proposed that such heart rate rises may be considered as signs of 'overtraining', whereby performance is reduced and the risk of injury is increased.

Conclusion

For optimal performance, runners must be experts in the tactical and technical side of the sport, be psychologically prepared to handle the enormous stress of critical situations, and be free from injury; they must also be physically 'fit'. Depending on the specific event, fitness in runners is a composite mainly associated with the efficiency of aerobic (i.e. with oxygen) and/or anaerobic (i.e. without oxygen) metabolism, muscle strength and muscle elasticity levels, and body composition. No fundamental differences have been noted between male and female runners with respect to fitness requirements, particularly when body dimensions and gender characteristics are taken into account. Last but not least, most of the fitness components discussed in this chapter may show considerable variations during different training and competition periods and such variations may depend on levels of running performance.

Nutrition and diet

by Janet Pidcock

Eating well will not only benefit your general health, but can also significantly improve your running performance. The type of food you eat can actually affect your stamina and ability to cope with the stresses and strains of regular training.

On average, those of us living in the industrialized West eat too much fat, and not enough fibre; experts have linked this eating pattern to a number of health problems including heart disease, certain cancers, gut problems and possibly diabetes. In terms of fat, the main culprit appears to be saturated fat – this is found mainly in animal-derived foods such as meat and full-fat dairy produce, and in foods prepared with a high proportion of fat, e.g. cakes, biscuits, pastry. Eating healthily doesn't mean leaving these foods out, but cutting down on them, and eating relatively more starchy carbohydrate-rich foods such as bread, pasta and rice.

Choose wholefood versions of these foods (i.e. wholemeal bread, brown rice and pasta) and you'll also be boosting your fibre intake. Fibre is found in plant-derived foods (e.g. cereals, vegetables, fruit), and in general, the less processing the food has been subjected to, the higher the fibre content will be.

These general guidelines for good health also hold true for good running performance. Trimming the fat in your diet and stepping up the carbohydrates has been shown in a number of research studies to improve stamina – why this should be, and tips on how to go about changing your diet in this way are described below. Other nutrition issues that runners need to be aware of are: the potential dangers of dehydration, and the best ways to prevent this occurring, and the question of whether vitamin and mineral supplements are necessary.

The carbohydrate connection

How can eating more potatoes translate into faster running times? The key is in understanding the different energy stores that the body burns to fuel physical activity. When you eat a meal, any excess energy (measured as calories) in the food is stored. As most of us are aware, the body's favourite way to store surplus calories is as fat. However, there is also a carbohydrate energy store, called glycogen – strings of sugar molecules threaded together which are stored in the muscles and liver. Glycogen can be made only from carbohydrates or sugars in the diet, and not in any appreciable amount from fat or protein. When fat and glycogen are used to fuel exercise, there is a difference in their character. Fat can provide energy at a slow and steady rate for very long periods of time; in contrast, glycogen is more flashy and can be converted rapidly into available energy, powering higher intensities of exercise, but running out sooner.

Thus, although the body has a fairly unlimited capacity to store fat, it is reluctant to hoard much glycogen. For a runner this will mean that when glycogen stores get low, the body will need to rely proportionately more on fat as an energy source. This can be experienced as a difficulty in maintaining initial pace, and an inability to push for a final sprint. The phrase 'hitting the wall' refers to this shift in fuel use. So the more glycogen you have to your name at the beginning of a run, the longer you'll be able to maintain your initial running speed.

Carbohydrate loading

The good news is that the body can be persuaded to store higher levels of glycogen. Researchers have found that eating a high-carbohydrate diet, combined with exercise, will encourage the muscles to stash away more glycogen. This effect was discovered in the late 1960s by Swedish researchers, who formalized a routine for achieving high glycogen levels; this has become known as 'carbohydrate loading'. The regime they developed involved training to exhaustion, followed by eating a diet high in fat and protein for three days (the bleed-out phase), then

switching to a very high carbohydrate diet for three days.

Experts now agree that the bleed-out element is unnecessarily extreme and risky, and have found that the same glycogen loading effect can be achieved by eating a high-carbohydrate diet for five days before a competition while tapering training. In one such research study, the tapering programme involved the last heavy exercise being undertaken a week before competing, followed by 90, 40, 20 and 20-minute exercise sessions on the respective following days. The day before competing was a day of complete rest.

Undertaking such a carbo-loading regime will probably be of benefit to anyone running for longer than 60 minutes (or 45 minutes if any gradient running is involved), as this is the time when glycogen reserves would start running low ordinarily. However, this nutrition strategy isn't something that should be tucked away only for use prior to competition. A number of studies have demonstrated that athletes on a medium-level carbohydrate diet who complete a number of consecutive training sessions end up draining their glycogen reserves.

Do you sometimes feel washed out at the end of the week, suffering from heavy, tired muscles and continuous lethargy? This, and the overtraining syndrome, may be due to failure to restock muscle glycogen stores between training sessions, so that you end up gradually draining them (see the graph). The results will be an inability to train optimally, and more risk of injury. A number of sports nutrition experts now advise runners to eat a high-carbohydrate diet the whole time, in order to keep glycogen levels topped up, and to just taper training before an event to boost the glycogen extra-high.

The evidence suggests that in general, athletes don't get enough carbohydrates to ensure their glycogen reserves are kept topped up during training. It's been estimated that runners need to eat between one-quarter and one-third more carbohydrates than the amount eaten by Mr or Ms Average. Research into runners' diets has found that most fail to meet this carbo target.

To give an idea of what this means in practice, a guideline is to aim for 8-10g carbohydrate per kg of body weight per day. For an average man (70kg), this would mean aiming at a daily intake of 560-700g; for an average woman (55kg), between 440-550g. The carbohydrate content of various foods is set out in the table, to give an idea of what quantities you would need to eat.

In general, however, don't get too hung up with the figures – you don't want to be poised over a calculator and weighing scales at mealtimes. There are two main guidelines which will help you achieve a high carb diet – one is to cut down on foods high in fat (remember, fat can't be converted into glycogen), and the other is to replace fatty food with starchy, carbohydrate-rich foods.

Don't worry if you've been told that carbohydrates are fattening – they're not.

Weight for weight, fat contains over half the calories of carbohydrate. Thus, for example, 100g of Cheddar cheese provides 406 calories, whereas 100g of boiled potato provides only 80. In addition, as carbohydrate foods tend to be bulkier than fatty foods, expect the actual size of a carbohydrate-rich meal to look larger!

The other trick to be aware of is that the body is at its most eager to store away glycogen soon after exercise. So it's worth having something carbohydrate-rich to eat or drink as soon as possible after a run – a carbohydrate-rich drink, or fresh or dried fruit if you can't face heavy food for a while.

The carbohydrate content of foods

Food	Amount	Carbohydrate (g)
Apple	1 medium	20
Orange	1 medium	20
Banana	1 medium	20
Muesli	½ cup	36
Apple juice	8 fl oz	30
Orange juice	8 fl oz	25
Baked potato	1 large	55
Baked beans	1 cup	50
Lentils	1 cup (cooked)	40
Spaghetti	1 cup (cooked)	40
Rice	1 cup (cooked)	35
Fruit yogurt	1 cup	35

Boosting your carbohydrate intake

The twin strategies are to cut back on fat and increase carbohydrates.

Fat trimmers
● Substitute semi-skimmed or skimmed milk for full-fat milk

● Choose low-fat dairy products: yogurt, cheese, spreads

● Choose poultry (without the skin) or fish rather than red meat

● Experiment with vegetable sources of protein: beans (e.g. red kidney beans, baked beans), grains (rice, oats, wheat), nuts and seeds

● Steam, poach or grill food rather than frying

● If you're frying food at home, try stir-frying (quickly, with a small amount of fat at a high temperature) to keep the fat content down

● Try to cut out the fats that traditionally go with carbo-rich foods – don't douse potatoes in butter, try sandwiches without butter, avoid dollops of mayonnaise with salads (try lemon juice and herbs instead)

● When eating sweet foods, avoid the ones that are also high in fat. Chocolates, biscuits and most cakes fall into this category

Carbo boosters
● Porridge made with water provides a high-carb start to the day

● Base meals around carbohydrate foods – potatoes, pasta, rice, etc.

● Eat smaller portions of fat-rich foods and fill up with extra potatoes, vegetables etc.

● If eating out, fill up with extra bread rather than choosing a fatty starter

● Use yogurt or fromage frais in place of cream

● Drink fruit juice with meals, and a milky drink at bed-time

● Cut bread extra-thick for sandwiches

● Try carbohydrate-rich snacks that are also low in fat: dried fruit, water biscuits

● Choose pasta sauces based on tomatoes or vegetables rather than meat or cheese

Fluid facts

An under-rated nutrient, water should be included as part of your nutrition strategy aiming you towards optimum performance. The risk of dehydration is something to take seriously – even moderate losses can mean operating at less

that 80 per cent of your potential. You can lose up to two litres of water an hour from sweat in a distance run. There is wide individual variation in fluid loss, but loss of only 2 per cent of your body weight as fluid can seriously affect your performance.

The fluid in sweat is borrowed from a number of sources within the body, the most critical of which is the fluid lost from blood plasma. The result is a smaller and more sluggish blood volume, which gets increasingly treacle-like the more dehydrated you get. The blood circulation carries out the essential task of supplying oxygen and fuel to your muscles. If this vital supply slows down, so will you. The heart will be put under pressure, and in serious cases of dehydration, medical complications can occur.

So how do you ensure that you stay sufficiently in the black as far as your fluid balance is concerned? For water to get into the bloodstream, it must get through the stomach, and cross the wall of the small intestine. Stomach emptying is slowed down by concentrated fluids, and solid food. Diluted drinks and water itself are the quickest to get through to the bloodstream.

You may have come across commercially formulated sports drinks making various claims. These can be simplified into three basic types: firstly, the **carbo boosters**, which are aimed at pre-competition, as an aid to carbo-loading. These can be beneficial as a top-up prior to competing; but don't rely on them to provide the bulk of your carbo needs, as you'll miss out on the other nutrients that starchy foods provide – certain vitamins and minerals, and fibre.

The two other main types of drinks are **hypotonics** and **isotonics**. These drinks are two points on a spectrum of drinks trying to fulfil two distinct functions. One is rehydration, the other is the provision of

It is important to drink fluid when racing in hot weather to avoid dehydration. You can lose up to two litres of water an hour just from sweating when on a distance run.

carbohydrate while exercising. To an extent, these two aims are mutually exclusive, as the more carbohydrate present, the slower the uptake of the fluid. Thus, hypotonic drinks (hypotonic means less concentrated than blood) are the fastest way to get fluid into the bloodstream – slightly faster than water, and worth considering if you're running in particularly hot conditions, or know that you have a tendency to sweat heavily. The carbohydrate provided is minimal, however.

By contrast, isotonic solutions are at the same concentration as blood, and are formulated to deliver the most carbohydrate possible without compromising the rate of fluid uptake (which will be similar to plain water).

Maltodextrins

Many of the isotonics currently available contain a special form of carbohydrate called maltodextrin. Maltodextrins are a way of sneaking more carbohydrate into a fluid without the body noticing, as far as speed of uptake is concerned. This is because the speed of fluid uptake is dependent on the number of molecules dissolved in a solution, rather than their size. Maltodextrin is a sugar polymer: a large molecule made up of strings of simple sugars (both glucose and fructose are examples of simple sugars) joined together. These molecules can then be broken back down into the simple sugars once they're in the bloodstream.

The advantage of this is that towards the end of a distance run (over an hour), having an additional, quickly absorbable source of sugar to provide energy will enable muscle glycogen stores to last

Running tip

The conditions on the day are crucial – if it's particularly hot, you'd be best going for plain water or a hypotonic; under more temperate conditions an isotonic may be best; when the weather's cold (and if you know you don't tend to sweat much), you could probably tolerate a drink more concentrated than an isotonic, and benefit from the higher levels of carbohydrate.

Running tip

You can make up your own sports drink which will bring about fast rehydration by adding a pinch of salt and 2-4g glucose per 100ml water. The salt and the glucose help the water to be transported more quickly into the bloodstream.

longer and therefore initial speed could be maintained for longer.

A number of trials have shown enhanced performance when athletes were given such isotonic drinks throughout a run. Some studies have failed to show an effect, however.

Some drinks claim to help replace the minerals lost in sweat. This is very misleading – although some minerals will be lost through sweating, the amounts are fairly small (with the possible exception of iron), and will easily be made up through eating normally. The sodium in sports drinks isn't there to replace salt lost in sweat, but because it encourages the body to absorb fluid more quickly.

Vitamins and minerals – added value?

Athletes are obsessive pill-poppers. The pills in question being dietary supplements, not drugs. One survey of America's top female runners found that 91 per cent regularly took some form of

Tips to keep dehydration at bay

● Ensure a high fluid intake for the last few days before competition. A useful check for adequate hydration is to ensure that your urine is pale in colour

● Don't drink alcohol the night before a race – it will dehydrate you

● Before competing, try to drink between ½ and ¾ pint 15 minutes beforehand

● Drink little and often. Aim for about ¼ pint every 15 minutes

● Practise drinking during your training, to get used to the feeling of running with fluid in your stomach

● Start drinking early on in a run. Thirst isn't a good enough indicator of dehydration – by the time you're feeling thirsty, you've already lost a significant amount of fluid. So drink before you feel thirsty

● If you decide you want to use a sports drink, try out several during training to work out which work the best for you

● Get into the habit of weighing yourself before and after events. This will indicate how much fluid you're losing. If you lose more than 2 per cent of your body weight, try to take in more fluids while competing

supplement. Studies in Britain have come up with more conservative figures of between 30-80 per cent, with women being more likely to take them than men.

In most cases, taking vitamin or mineral supplements will have little effect unless your diet is so poor you're getting low levels in the first place. As many vitamins and minerals are intimately involved with the body's processes of energy production, a simplistic theory might be that taking extra- large doses would lead to a more abundant energy supply! In fact, the body is more complex than this, and large doses of vitamins can end up having different effects from those seen at normal levels of intake. For example, large doses of niacin (vitamin B3) have been shown in some studies to reduce the availability of free fatty acids (an important energy source) during exercise, and high doses of B6 may lead to more rapid using up of glycogen stores – a very undesirable effect for a distance runner.

A combination of vitamins which has been the focus of a number of sports science research studies are vitamins A (in a form called B-carotene), C and E. When taken together as a cocktail, it's possible that these vitamins protect against a particular type of cellular stress induced by endurance events. It's been suggested therefore that taking this combination of vitamins could reduce muscle damage (the evidence so far is tenuous). It must be noted, however, that high doses of vitamin A (not in the B-carotene form) can be highly toxic.

Vitamins B1 and B2 (Thiamine and Riboflavin) help convert food into energy, and the amounts needed are thought to increase with exercise. The generally higher food intake that goes along with increased physical exercise will usually take care of this. The danger could be if a lot of refined carbohydrates were being eaten (white rice, flour, pasta, etc.) as the wholefood versions are far higher than in these B vitamins.

In general, taking high doses of vitamins has not been convincingly demonstrated to improve performance unless there was a prior deficiency. Megadoses of the water-soluble vitamins (B and C) are generally safe, as is B-carotene and vitamin E; however, taking high doses of the fat-soluble vitamins A or D is potentially hazardous and not recommended.

Your best bet is to try and get all the vitamins and minerals you need from your food. In general, the closer a food is to its natural state, the higher it will be in vitamins and minerals. Wholefoods and foods eaten raw or lightly cooked will have the highest vitamin and mineral content.

Keep your iron balance in the red!

The only mineral that has been demonstrated convincingly to improve athletic performance is iron, and this is because runners have an increased tendency to anaemia. So common is the problem that medics have a special category called runner's anaemia. A number of factors are thought to contribute to increased losses of iron in distance runners.

The action of running may stress the bladder and kidneys and lead to small amounts of bleeding, with resultant loss of iron in the urine. High sweat losses can mean increased iron losses. Runners may have some bleeding from the gut – this may be because of constant jarring of the colon. Direct trauma to the muscles (in particular, the foot muscles being pounded) leads to some destruction of blood cells. It's also possible that endurance runners don't absorb iron so well from the gut.

Three progressive stages of iron deficiency have been defined:

● Firstly, stores of iron (these are called ferritin) become low.

● Secondly, haemoglobin levels decrease (haemoglobin is an iron-containing protein which carries oxygen in the red blood cell).

● Thirdly, once haemoglobin gets below a certain level (12g/dl for women, 10g/dl for men), anaemia is diagnosed.

Evidence has shown that athletes with low storage iron levels can suffer from impaired performance even before their haemoglobin has dropped below the critical values.

So, what can you do if you suspect that you're iron deficient? Iron supplements are available, and taking some for a few days to see if you notice any improvement could help identify if you really are deficient. However, supplements are commonly associated with side-effects such as nausea, heartburn and stomach discomfort, so your best bet is to try and boost your iron intake by dietary means. Even if you don't suffer immediate side-effects, you should seek medical advice before taking an iron supplement regularly, because it's possible to suffer long-term side effects from too much iron!

The best dietary sources of iron are organ meat (e.g. liver) and red meat. There are vegetable sources of iron too but these are absorbed less easily. Absorption from

these sources increases if you eat them at the same time as meat. But if you don't eat meat, or are trying to cut down, don't despair, as there is another way to help raise vegetable iron absorption, and that's to eat something rich in vitamin C at the same time.

Ergogenic aids assessed

A number of substances have been touted to athletes for their ergogenic properties – such items are claimed to enhance performance beyond levels normally attainable. In the nutritional arena, substances will fall into one of the following three categories:

1 High doses of essential nutrients, e.g. vitamin megadoses – defined as anything above 10 times the Dietary Reference Value for a given vitamin.

2 Extra amounts of substances made naturally by the body, e.g. enzymes, or chemicals such as aspartate, which the body makes in the process of converting food into energy.

3 Substances that are neither essential nutrients nor chemicals naturally occurring in the body, e.g. caffeine, or the chemicals found in ginseng.

Beat the GI blues

Gastro-intestinal problems are all too common for the runner. Not suffered by other endurance athletes, such as cyclists, the problem is probably caused by repeated jolting of the gut while running. Here are

---

Boosting iron intake

● Tea and coffee interfere with the absorption of iron, so it's best to avoid drinking these at mealtimes.

● Include small amounts of red meat and/or organ meat in your diet. Eat dark poultry meat

● Vegetable iron sources include dark green vegetables, wholegrain cereals (pasta, flour, bread), pulses (e.g. red kidney beans, chickpeas, baked beans) and cocoa

● Avoid unprocessed bran, as this inhibits iron absorption

● Eat vegetable sources rich in vitamin C to help iron absorption. Vitamin C is found in fresh fruits and vegetables, so include a sliced tomato in sandwiches, eat a side-salad of raw vegetables, or drink a glass of orange juice with meals

● Choose breakfast cereals that are fortified with iron

---

some tips that some runners find helpful:

● Try liquid food only for the last meal before a long run or pre-competition. You could make this up yourself, or buy a commercially prepared liquid meal (make sure it's high in carbohydrate).

● Take care not to become dehydrated while running. Research has found that runners who take on board adequate fluid while running are less likely to suffer from gut problems.

● Avoid food high in fat or protein before your training run, as research shows that these are more likely to induce nausea if eaten before exercise.

● Some people find that decreasing the fibre content of their diet before competing improves things.

Ergogenic aids

Vitamins/Minerals

Category/name	Claim	Evidence
B12	Megadoses (taken by injection) enhance performance	Poor
Phosphate salts	Fatigue reduction	Positive findings in early studies haven't been confirmed. Large doses may increase risk of calcium deficiency

Substances occurring naturally in the body

Aspartate	Speeds up energy production	No evidence of benefit to trained athletes
Carnitine	Speeds up conversion of fats into energy	Evidence sparse
Coenzyme Q	Improved endurance	Animal studies but no convincing research on humans
Branched-chain amino acids (leucine, iso-leucine and valine	Energy source that could improve endurance	Some evidence of benefit; however, long-term effects unknown
Creatine	Beneficial in short-term exercise (less than 10 minutes, e.g. sprinting)	Emerging evidence of a definite effect

Substances foreign to the body

Ginseng	Improved endurance performance	Animal studies showing benefits haven't been convincingly reproduced in humans. Long-term use may have undesirable side-effects, e.g. high blood pressure
Caffeine	Improved endurance performance, possibly via an adrenaline-like effect	Appears to have a beneficial effect on some athletes – this may be enhanced if caffeine is abstained from for 4 days. Some will suffer unwelcome side-effects (e.g. gut problems). Carbo-loading may negate the effect
Wheat germ oil	Component called octasanol claimed to enhance endurance	Research evidence reviewed by the American Federal Trade Commission was found to be unconvincing; ads for the supplement claiming enhanced sports performance were banned

Running injuries treatment

by Patrick Milroy

By the very nature of the running action most injuries found in distance runners occur to the lower limbs and back and these are the areas to be discussed in detail. In this chapter, we are not going to deal with disease of the whole body that may make it unwise for certain individuals to run. Some conditions, such as asthma, may well be helped by running. However, if a potential runner has a medical problem or condition, they should seek advice from a general practitioner before taking up the sport.

In all branches of medicine, prevention is often easier than cure, and this is certainly the case with runners' injuries. Time and thought spent on planning clothing, shoes and training may well prevent the frustration that injury can cause.

Running is a complex mechanical action of the body involving many movements, which do, however, have a common principle involving the alternate contraction and relaxation of muscles – the meat of the body. These are attached by thinner silvery tendons to two bones, which themselves are in contact at a joint – an enclosed space filled with synovial fluid which oils the movement of one bone against the other.

On this basis, you can see that a torn muscle in the thigh will involve the same pattern of treatment and rehabilitation as one in the calf, so before detailing with specific injuries it is important to understand how the individual elements work and in what way they may become damaged.

The running body

Muscle damage in runners commonly occurs as a result of sudden internal stretching forces tearing muscle fibres, the connective tissues and blood vessels. This may extend either partially or completely through the muscle, and the resultant bleeding within the muscle will cause a rise in tension and pain if it is contracted. Muscle bundles are enclosed in a sheath which, if torn, will allow the blood to escape. In a partial rupture this is not the case and the ensuing internal bruise, or haematoma, causes pain and a reduction in the ability of the muscle to contract or be passively stretched. Ideally, in order to minimize the damage, any treatment

141

should be immediate. Cold from an ice pack and then pressure bandaging will prevent internal bleeding whilst elevation of the limb and rest will decrease the pressure from local blood flow. After two days, when the bleeding has ceased, healing can be expedited by an increase in the blood flow using physiotherapy and some graduated active exercise.

After injury the haematoma is invaded by repair cells which lay down inelastic scar tissue. If this is untreated it may shorten the muscle permanently. Total recovery is thus dependent upon progressive mobilization and stretching of the muscle to increase flexibility of the neighbouring joints. A shortened muscle has less power, thereby putting extra

stresses on other parts of the body which, in turn, can lead to secondary injury.

Tendons link muscles to bone and consist of bands of collagen fibres surrounded by a paratendon, outside which is a further tendon sheath. Like muscles, the tendons may split under sudden stretching and this tear may be either complete or partial.

The tendon, paratendon and tendon sheath may also become inflamed and hence swollen, causing a tendonitis, peritendonitis or tenovaginitis respectively. It is the tension of the swelling that causes the pain and this is discussed in the section dealing with Achilles tendon injuries. (see page 144).

Bones are not commonly injured through running except as the result of a

The synovial joint

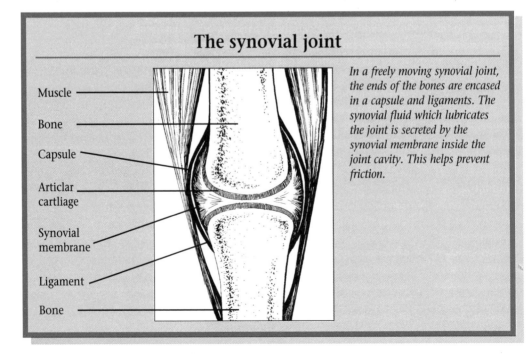

Muscle

Bone

Capsule

Articlar cartliage

Synovial membrane

Ligament

Bone

In a freely moving synovial joint, the ends of the bones are encased in a capsule and ligaments. The synovial fluid which lubricates the joint is secreted by the synovial membrane inside the joint cavity. This helps prevent friction.

stress fracture, which may occur with a sudden increase in training load, though pain is not invariably felt at once. Any pain is usually localized and a tender spot may be palpated, but the diagnosis is not always clear as X-ray changes may not appear for several weeks.

The bones most affected are the tibiae and the metatarsal bones of the foot. These fractures must be rested, at the physician's discretion, sometimes in plaster, so that symptoms may subside and training can be resumed cautiously and progressively after a few weeks.

Most **joints** within the limbs have the same basic structure. Each knee also contains internally two half moon-shaped cartilages and ligaments. It is not common for joints to lock in runners, unless a loose body of bone from an underlying disease such as arthritis is floating within it.

However, an increase in synovial fluid with swelling of the joint may well occur after the demands placed on it by road or long-distance racing. This sign of chronic inflammation is particularly likely in the older runner and an expert medical opinion must be sought.

In a sprain, excessive movement of the joint damages the capsule or a ligament. The ankle is particularly vulnerable in cross-country runners, with pain, swelling and protective muscle spasm. This type of injury will need a longer period of rest and even immobilization before active training can be resumed. Some strapping may be needed initially in training, but must be progressively discarded before competition.

A **bursa** is a protective lubricating sac of fluid found where tendons or muscles move over a prominent bone. If these become inflamed by excessive rubbing they may swell and form a bursitis.

They need early treatment with physiotherapy and anti-inflammatory medication to prevent them becoming chronically inflamed. If this happens, surgical removal may be necessary to effect a cure.

Causes of injury

Not all injuries are preventable, but there are certain factors that may make injury more likely, these being:

● **Congenital deformities** may be noticed only as a result of running. Recurring knee pain may be due to a genu varum, or bow leg, which may be corrected easily by wedging the outer side of the shoe heels. In many cases of chronic knee pain the only abnormality may be a genu valgum, or knock-knee, which can be associated with excessive pronation of the foot. Limb length discrepancy may cause pain from the back downwards. Correction requires accurate measurements of the limb by a competent physician with a built-up shoe to compensate for the asymmetrical stride. Although a minority may need podiatric advice and an orthotic device, simple first aid with a sorbothane heel wedge can effect an almost miraculous recovery by equalizing the leg lengths.

Running shoe problems

When a runner pronates (far right) the foot and shoe tilt inwards and this can lead to injury, especially in the shins and knees. Good shoes, special inserts and orthotic devices can help to prevent and alleviate this problem.

- **Training** is discussed elsewhere, but unless it is stepped up *gradually*, over-use injuries will occur.

- **Running surfaces** Too much running is performed on hard and uneven roads. The effect on the body of always running on one side of a cambered road will cause forces similar to those found in the congenital deformities. Running uphill places excess strain on the Achilles tendon; running downhill on the thigh muscles. The intelligent runner will alternate between running on roads and soft paths or grass, and mix in some hill work judiciously.

- **Shoes** must be well-fitting and comfortable. Thick-soled shoes with broad, flared heels will absorb much of the runner's impact, whereas the thin-soled

flat racing shoes offer little protection between foot and ground and are a potent cause of injury.

Runners who pronate excessively usually benefit from a straight lasted shoe or one that prevents the shoe tilting inwards. The ideal shoe has a high rounded toe box to protect the toes and nails, a flexible mid-sole helping to prevent Achilles problems, an arch support for metatarsal pain and a well padded tongue to lessen irritation on the extensor tendons beneath. Heel tabs are discussed under Achilles tendon injuries.

Achilles tendon injuries

The tendon, connecting the calf muscles to the heel, causes more distress to runners than any other injury. Some of the most common problems and their treatments are discussed below.

- **A complete rupture** is felt suddenly as a blow on the heel and the runner is lame. He is unable to stand on the toes of that foot and it is usually possible to feel a gap in the tendon. It is now usual to repair this surgically, although some specialists still prefer to put the ankle in a plaster cast for several weeks to heal naturally.

- **A partial rupture** is felt as a pain in the tendon which recurs every time the runner pushes off from his toes. It often occurs with a sudden change in pace during a race. The scar tissue formed during healing is often painful and may require surgical removal, although some partial ruptures will respond to rest and careful physiotherapy and stretching.

- **Simple tendonitis** may occur after unaccustomed strenuous exercise and is associated with local pain and tenderness but no swelling or crepitus (a feeling of 'crackling' in the tendon as the ankle is alternately moved backwards and forwards). Heel wedging and a few days' rest are required to prevent the injury becoming chronic.

- In **peritendonitis** there is swelling and crepitus especially in the lower two inches of the tendon.

- **Achilles bursitis**, or Pump Bump, is caused by irritation of shoes against the calcaneus. It is felt as a tender nodule lateral to the lower attachment of the Achilles and if it fails to settle with the measures listed below it may need a steroid injection or surgery to remove it.

- **Treatments** include physiotherapy, a cold compress initially to reduce inflammation and stop any bleeding, followed by ultra-sound or short-wave. Friction rubbing should not be used, as it only causes extra inflammation. A doctor may prescribe anti-inflammatory drugs but more chronic causes may need steroid (cortisone) injections into the tendon sheath, though never the tendon itself. Despite the bad press these injections have sometimes received, they do have a place in treatment by an experienced sports physician.

If the Achilles injury is the result of excessive pronation, an orthotic device may be needed to support the longitudinal arch of the foot. Continued stretching exercises are vital, even if the injury is quiescent, if it is not to recur. Trying to 'run through' Achilles tendonitis may convert a mild injury into a chronic one with subsequently increased damage and a greater risk that surgery will be required.

- **Causes and prevention** Achilles problems may be prevented in many cases by simple padding to raise the heel, adequate warm-up and stretching exercises. Occasional calf massage also helps, and regular calf stretching, especially before running, is essential. The so-called 'heel protectors', the high heel tabs found in many running shoes, may do exactly the opposite. If when wearing the shoes and pointing the toes the heel tabs dig into the tendon, they will give a microscopic

The main bones and muscles of the leg

The bones

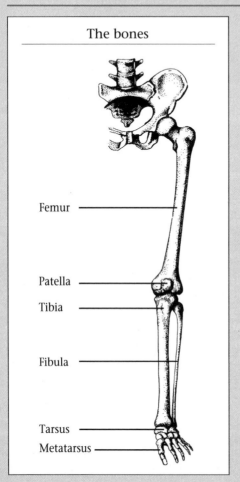

Femur

Patella

Tibia

Fibula

Tarsus

Metatarsus

The muscles

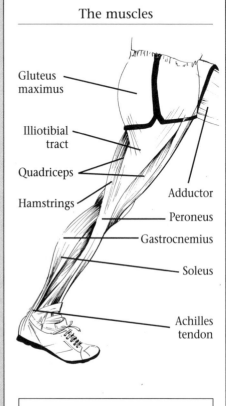

Gluteus maximus

Illiotibial tract

Quadriceps

Hamstrings

Adductor

Peroneus

Gastrocnemius

Soleus

Achilles tendon

Achilles tendon

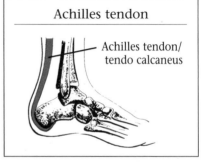

Achilles tendon/ tendo calcaneus

The illustration (above) shows the bones and also the muscles of the legs. A detail of the Achilles tendon, a common area for injury is shown (inset), together with the tendon sheath. Muscles are made of contractile tissue and give the legs their strength and mobility when running.

bruise with every step. In this case the only course is to refashion the back of the shoe by cutting off the heel tab. In the past it would appear that shoe manufacturers were unwilling to accept this problem for fear of litigation, but now many shoes have no tab or a cut out.

Leg injuries

● **Ankle sprains** are common, often with sufficient pain and swelling to make one suspect a fracture. If there is an internal sprain 'inside the joint capsule' the joint may need the fluid aspirating, followed by rest with extensive mobilization to prevent a stiff joint forming. As well as conventional physiotherapy a 'wobble-board' may be of great benefit, and this can be easily made by taking a wooden board two feet square and nailing two concave pieces of wood underneath.

● **Shin splints** may have several causes which should be differentiated. In the anterior compartment syndrome the muscles between the two longer leg bones become swollen if the beginner steps up his training too fast, and reduce their own blood supply. Rest, ice and elevation may alleviate this, but if it becomes chronic surgical decompression may be necessary to save the muscle dying for lack of blood.

● In **periostitis** pain occurs on the inner border of the shin bone which may be acutely tender to touch. It is due to muscle pulling away from the bone and weak scar tissue forming which again pulls away

from the bone with even minimal exercise. Rest, ice and taping the leg followed by alternating hot and cold soaks must be used before returning to training on soft level ground. Again the shoes may need a wedge or orthotic device to prevent the hyperpronation which is often responsible.

● **Stress fractures** of the tibia and fibula have already been discussed and must be suspected if shin splints fail to settle. These injuries can be prevented generally by avoiding sudden increases in your running activity.

● **Foot pain** This can often be a simply corrected problem. Shoes have been discussed elsewhere, but where feet are of unequal sizes it is better to buy a pair in which the larger foot is comfortable and to pad the other internally rather than using a shoe that is too tight.

Each foot has two arches, both a longitudinal and transverse, and pain frequently occurs if these become flattened, altering the mechanics of foot movement.

● In **Morton's foot**, the second toe is longer than the first, so that it is both prone to trauma and to the pressures of acting as a fulcrum for the whole foot. As such it can develop a stress fracture and require the use of an orthotic to spread the load away from the toe.

● **Metatarsalgia** is very often due to wearing tight or incorrectly laced training shoes and responds to wider fitting and a transverse arch support.

● **Hallux rigidus**, an osteoarthritis of the first metatarsophalangeal joint, is also a runner's complaint as it reduces forefoot mobility and causes rigid splinting of the foot. If it is not corrected by a metatarsal support surgery may prove necessary.

● **Plantar fasciitis** is an acutely painful condition of the underside of the foot in which both a high or dropped longitudinal arch may be implicated. If support for the arch or removal of the pressure point with heel pads fail to cure it, it generally responds to a steroid injection.

Other leg injuries

● *Chondromalacia patellae*, or **'runner's knee'**, is by far the commonest cause of knee pain in runners. Without going into all the anatomical complexities the patella normally runs in a groove at the bottom of the femur as the knee is flexed and extended. However, because the hips are separated compared to the ankles and knees, there is a lateral force on the patella as the knee is extended, which rubs it against the outside of the joint.

The pain is typically described by the novice runner increasing his mileage as an aching around the kneecap, aggravated by climbing stairs, though easing with training, only to recur later in the day. The kneecaps may appear to 'squint' at one another when the feet are placed side by side.

Treatment initially must consist of ice, rest and aspirin. Further improvement is obtained by strengthening the quadriceps muscles – especially the medial ones. This is done by lying on a bed, the knee held straight, lifting gradually increasing

weights, from 1lb/450g to 8lb/3.6kg suspended from the ankles. The weights should be lifted up to one hundred times a day until the pain disappears, and only then may running be recommended. Training should avoid hills and still be allied with the above quadriceps exercises and suitable orthotic devices. Surgery is only needed in the most extreme cases.

Other causes of knee pain are not peculiar to runners but may still occur in the athlete. Knee pain may be a sign of injury elsewhere, though cartilage injuries in particular are rare solely due to running.

● **Hamstring** tears may appear suddenly during any speedwork, but more commonly develop insidiously due to inadequate stretching before and after training. The usual application of ice and rest are vital until pain subsides. When rehabilitation is started, ultrasound, coupled with gentle active exercises, should restore full fitness.

Much hamstring pain may be referred from the back, causes from a slipped disc to a sacro-iliac strain being implicated. Runners should not be surprised if investigation of recurrent hamstring pain includes a full spinal assessment.

● **Calf muscle tears** are treated no differently to hamstrings, and prevention by stretching is much easier than treating the strained muscle.

● **Adductor** strains may occur if a runner has to take a large stride as in steeplechase or cross-country races. The pain is felt on the inner upper side of the thigh as the stretch is made. Energetic physiotherapy with ultrasound and adductor stretching exercises will usually effect a cure, but in severe cases manipulation under general anaesthetic is required.

The principal problem is in differentiating this from other pain in the groin. Osteitis pubis is a pain between the two pubic bones caused by the shearing action of the bones on each other. Rest and steroids may be required. Runners are not exempt from inguinal herniae or hip disease, which can also cause pain in this region.

General injuries and health problems

● **Sciatica** is potentially serious in runners, nerve compression causing back, buttock and/or leg pain. It appears to be exacerbated by an uneven running gait and running on downhill surfaces which transmit excess shock through the spine. Although a few days of rest and anti-inflammatory tablets may settle the condition if only the joint between the vertebrae is injured, an intervertebral disc prolapse (slipped disc) must be excluded to avoid any potentially disastrous nerve damage.

● **Stitch** appears to occur most commonly in the unfit runner who trains too soon after a meal or takes inappropriate drinks whilst running. Many causes are suggested, including spasm of the diaphragmatic muscles. It is treated by abdominal strengthening exercises, trunk curls or step-ups and by allowing two or three hours between eating and running. If it occurs

during a race, it may be possible to avoid stopping by bending forwards and holding your breath or twisting your trunk.

● **Stiffness** is universal, associated with unaccustomed running, but of unknown cause. A good warm-up is essential in prevention, although some people have a definite propensity to stiffness, uncommon in others. A hot bath and the occasional use of aspirin will ease it, though no runner should train under the influence of anti-inflammatory medication. Long, slow distance training appears to be more

The sciatic nerve

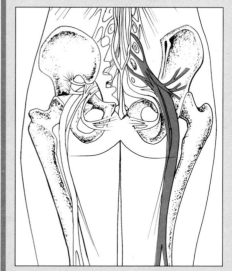

Sciatic pain occurs when the sciatic nerves at the base of the spine, which serve the legs, are pinched or irritated. It may be caused by excessive speedwork or uneven running. Regular stretching exercises can help prevent this condition.

Tip: Stretching

You should never skimp on warm-up and stretching – even though your mind might feel ready to start running, your body will not, as it will need some gentle preparation for action before you leap out of the front door. Scientific studies have shown that a warm-up will help to increase the maximum oxygen capacity and heart rate and reduce lactic acid in the muscles. It releases tension and relaxes and stretches tight muscles. If you spend 10-15 minutes warming-up, perform all the exercises slowly and smoothly as jerky and quick movements will do more harm than good and may even tighten already tense muscles. Any stretch should at most be uncomfortable, never painful, and should be held in a static position – 30 seconds is probably the ideal. Do not 'rock', as a muscle tear is the inevitable sequel. It is also important to warm-down after the run as it can reduce stiffness and help slow the heart rate back down to its normal level. Self-massage in the bath or shower can also help relax muscles.

effective in prevention but so many distance runners are inherently stiff (e.g. they cannot touch their toes) that they would benefit considerably from flexibility exercises and weekly reduction in mileage.

● **Haemoglobinuria** is well recognised in distance runners who do a lot of road work. Whilst all runners who appear to have blood in the urine should be investigated, it is usually benign and should not hinder training.

● **Heat injury** is not uncommon despite the British climate. If sweat losses do not match the increase in body core temperature from muscle-generated heat, air temperature or rise in relative humidity, cramps, exhaustion or heat stroke may supervene.

Heat cramps require rest and replace ment of fluid and electrolytes. The signs of heat exhaustion are light-headedness, confusion, nausea, vomiting and cramps. The skin is cold and clammy, the pulse rapid but weak. Runners with these symptoms should be made to drop out of the race and cooled in the shade and rehydrated urgently, if necessary by the use of intravenous fluids.

Severe heat stroke may be fatal, with fits and loss of consciousness occurring in addition to the above symptoms. Acclimatization, adequate pre-race fluid intake, brief, light, loose clothing, a lower pace and sufficient drinks during the race should be preventive measures. Many runners like to take pre-race salt tablets on hot days, though this is probably of little value.

● **Cold injury** shows itself as incoordin-ation, confusion and lethargy. Sensible clothing, covering the exposed parts with petroleum jelly, and rapid post-race warming should help to prevent it.

Skin

● **Blisters** occur when the layers of the skin become detached from each other, the gap being filled with a watery fluid from the damaged cells. They are usually due to ill-fitting or new shoes. Treatment should consist of releasing the fluid with a sterilized needle, snipping away the dead skin and applying tincture of iodine and a dry dressing. Repeated blistering can be prevented by using foot powder, soft insoles and two pairs to socks to prevent friction.

● **Athletes foot** is a common fungus infection and can be diagnosed easily. It is favoured by a moist warm environment and is particularly common between the toes. Prevention by frequent changes of socks – preferably cotton – avoidance of plastic or sweaty training shoes, and the liberal application of foot powder is often more effective than treatment. Tolnaftate and Clotrimazole creams are both obtainable without prescription, but recurrences are common and it may be necessary to paint the affected area with Castellani's Paint.

● **Tinea Cruris** is a similar fungal infection of the groin often found when the underwear is not washed sufficiently frequently. Most of the remarks about athletes foot also apply. However, treatment may require an anti-fungal cream combined with a mild steroid – available only on prescription – never a steroid cream alone.

• **Ingrowing toe nails** are usually accompanied by an infection of the nail fold. They are associated with tight training shoes and badly cut nails. First aid is by trying to 'jack-up' the affected nail using thin slivers of silver paper. The nails should be cut square rather than in a semi-circular fashion and a small V-shaped nick in the middle may encourage the nail to grow inwards. Treatment may require antibiotics to be prescribed, but it can prove necessary to have a small operation to remove part of the toe nail or to insert a small plastic guard along the side of the toe nail for two to three months.

• **Joggers nipple** is characterized by tenderness, chafing or even bleeding. Prevention is by covering the nipples with petroleum jelly or a plaster before the event, whereas treatment relies on an antiseptic cream or, if severe, a corn-pad type of protection.

Summary

The treatment and prevention of running injuries are usually based on conservative measures. Almost invariably a reduction in the training mileage or rest is called for, depending on the type of injury, but this may also be helped by a change of shoes, running surface and the type of training carried out.

When pain is relatively mild after injury, the application of ice for ten minutes, the elevation of the injured part and stretching exercises may help. These should be followed later in the day by warmth and more stretching. If this fails to settle the injury after a few days, then the advice of a doctor or a qualified physiotherapist should be sought.

Prevention of injuries is all about flexibility of the joints and it is almost impossible to do too many loosening and stretching exercises both before and after running. Many exercises done against resistance will prevent imbalance injuries, whereas heel wedging or the rather more expensive orthotic devices will compensate for many of the congenital and bio-mechanical causes of injury.

When an injury is severe it may prove necessary for a doctor to prescribe oral non-steroidal anti-inflammatory medication. This should be taken as prescribed and not as and how the runner feels. If a steroid (cortisone) injection is required, the benefits may be almost magical, but it must be administered by a doctor familiar with sports injuries. Although mentioned above as the ultimate treatment for many injuries, surgery is rarely required, and the general fitness brought about by running usually ensures that the experienced runner has less need of a doctor than his or her flab-fighting contemporaries.

The role of physiotherapy

by Sandra Dyson

Physiotherapy is the use of physical, mechanical and electrical methods to restore the body to its original state after injury. The body will usually heal quite well without any outside help, but unfortunately most athletes cannot wait for this to happen naturally as they would be missing important training time or a vital race. Physiotherapy in its simplest form is when the runner is able to treat his own injury. There are many injuries which can be treated successfully at home, particularly if that treatment starts early – as soon after the injury as possible.

Usually the first sign of an injury is that the runner feels pain. Very often there will also be subsequent swelling at the site of damage, particularly if it involves a joint. If the swelling were allowed to go unattended then, apart from increased pain, there would be a very definite danger of the swelling becoming permanent. One of the most important factors that an athlete should remember, as a first aid after injury, are the vital letters I.C.E.

I is for ice or anything which is cold in an emergency – frozen peas or even cold water. The ice should be left in place for 10

minutes and then removed, but may be re-applied several times subsequently, with at least one hour between applications. It is important that the correct time be adhered to when applying an ice pack. Don't think that if ten minutes is good for the injury then half an hour must be better – it isn't.

C is for compression. After an injury, apart from a certain amount of bleeding of the damaged part which usually takes place, a watery fluid is often produced surrounding the injured part. The principal object of this fluid is to stop more bleeding and prevent any infection; it also provides a very useful, immediate and natural 'splinting' of the injured part, so that it is kept fairly immobile and prevents any further damage. It is a good idea to carry a crêpe bandage in your sports bag as a matter of routine. The bandage should be applied so that it is reasonably tight and will not slip off, but is not uncomfortable. If it is too tight, the circulation of the blood will be restricted and the injury made worse. Try to buy an elasticated, tubular bandage of the correct size. This is usually better because it supports the injury site with a uniform pressure and does not tighten or slacken as the patient moves about.

E is for elevation or raising the injured part. Swelling occurs after an injury, which must be removed somehow and it will be absorbed gradually into the blood vessels and lymph vessels. If the injury is in the leg and swelling is allowed to go unchecked, it will descend to the foot and make that swell also. If, however, the patient sits or lies with the injured leg raised, the effect of gravity will be to draw the blood away from the injury site and allow it to be carried away in the circulatory system. This allows the injury to heal more quickly and will be much less painful.

It is quite simple to apply all three aspects of I.C.E. at the same time. Put on a bandage, lie on the floor (if it is a leg injury) with the leg resting on a chair or sofa, and apply an ice pack for 10 minutes. According to the severity of the swelling, leave the leg elevated for between 30 minutes and one hour – but remove the ice pack after 10 minutes. If these first-aid procedures are adhered to, the physiotherapy is made much easier and you will be back in training more quickly. It is then possible to make an assessment of the injury and to select the most appropriate form of treatment.

By using first-aid, you have already taken care of the first two of the five aspects concerned with treating an injury:

1 Relief of pain.
2 Reduction of swelling.
3 Regaining of mobility.
4 Increased strength.
5 Rehabilitation.

By following the advice given in this chapter, you can then take care of the other three aspects of recovery. However, if there isn't a good response, you should, if possible, seek help from a qualified physiotherapist. Now let us have a look at eight of the most common conditions from which runners suffer.

Achilles tendon pain –Tenosynovitis

How to identify
Achilles tendon pain is a condition that affects many runners, mostly from the road or track fraternity. There are three conditions. The most common form of Achilles tendon pain is that caused by tenosynovitis which is inflammation of the tendon sheath. With this condition you will usually find that the first few steps you take in the morning as you get out of bed; will be very painful then as you continue to move around, the pain lessens. The same thing happens when you go training. To start with there is quite a lot of pain and then, as you 'warm up', it eases, which is unfortunate because the temptation is to continue training. However, if you do so then you pay the penalty next morning when it is even more sore, very gradually worsening day by day, until eventually the pain won't go however much 'warm up' you do.

If you sit with the Achilles tendon

relaxed, then by firmly pinching the tendon you will be able to locate the painful area. This will be in the neck of the tendon if the cause is tenosynovitis, and often some thickening or swelling will be noticed. If the condition is tenosynovitis, there are several things you must do:

1 Treat the symptoms.
2 Reduce the aggravation.
3 If possible, eliminate the cause.

How to treat

There are three useful ways of treating the symptoms – with ice, anti-inflammatory cream and with deep frictions.

Apply the ice or a proprietory cold pack at least three times each day. In the morning, at tea time and just before going to bed, is a good spacing. After applying the ice put on some of the anti-inflammatory cream. Deep frictions can be very effective. Most people will find that one border is more tender than the other, so on that border apply the frictions.

Position your leg so that the tendon is tautened, then with your fingers or with your thumb, whichever you find easier, rub hard across the tendon – not along it. Persevere for 5 minutes each day.

A lot of the aggravation to the tendon comes with the first few steps each morning and two ways to reduce this are:
1 Stretch the tendon whilst still lying in bed by drawing your toes up towards your knee and holding for a few seconds. About half a dozen of these should suffice.
2 Have a pair of shoes by the bed, with a decent-sized heel, that can be slipped

Tenosynovitis

 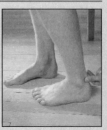

Above left: Test for tenosynovitis by firmly pinching the relaxed Achilles tendon as described in the text. Above right: To treat tenosynovitis, rub hard with fingers or thumb across the tautened achilles tendon.

on before any steps are taken. This limits the range through which the tendon is working.

It is a very good idea to reduce the amount of shock transmitted to the tendon when either walking or running by wearing heel inserts made from one of the shock absorbing compounds.

Apart from reducing the transmitted shock, it is necessary to reduce the range over which the tendon is used during the day. This can be done by wearing shoes with a good-sized heel and, if required, increasing that by wearing heel raises. These are best cut from a sheet of chiropody felt of 10mm thickness. You can use the heel inserts as templates. Always wear the inserts in both shoes even though only one tendon may be affected.

Whilst treating the symptoms it is as well at first to rest from running but most people find that cycling does not create any symptoms. It is also a good way of keeping up your fitness. As the symptoms improve you can return to running, but only gradually. Start by using flat grassland, progressively moving onto road, then hills. For those of you concerned with the track, your running will have to be in trainers initially, because the lack of decent heel with spiked shoes leads to a lot of unwanted stretching of the tendon.

Often it is impossible to find the cause of tenosynovitis but do check the more obvious possibilities such as unstable running shoes, or pressure from the heel tab onto the tendon. If pressure seems to be the cause, then though it may seem drastic, cutting off the heel tab of the shoe is very effective. Other than these mechanical problems, look for increases in volume of training or changes in type of training or even a change of surface as possible causes.

Achilles tendon – musculotendinous junction

How to identify

If pinching the neck of the tendon does not hurt but pressure higher up the calf does, then the source of the pain is likely to be damage in the musculotendinous junction. The symptoms behave in a similar way to those of tenosynovitis but the lessening of pain after warm-up is not as pronounced and often will come back during the session.

Because of this similarity the best help for diagnosis is the location of the pain, which will be below the belly of the muscle but above the slim part of the tendon.

How to treat

Once you have satisfied yourself that this is your problem then treating the symptoms can start. Treatment is somewhat different from that used in tenosynovitis so it is important to be sure. Deep massage is again very effective but with this condition you need to have the tendon relaxed. So place your leg in such a position. You can now apply the massage deeply and across

the fibres for 5 minutes each day. Heat has to be applied each day as well, for 15 minutes. A hot water bottle is very good.

This condition is usually the result of an abrupt strain – perhaps your heel dropping into a hollow and over-stretching the fibres. Once the symptoms have cleared it is unlikely that there will be any recurrence.

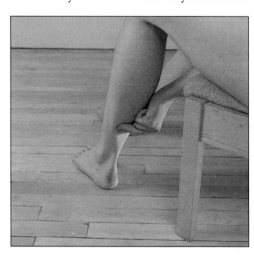

To treat musculotendinous junction, keep the tendon relaxed and massage deeply across the fibres.

Stretching exercises

These four stretching exercises need to be performed each day. As with all stretching exercises it has to be a slow process, with no bouncing.

Carry out each of the exercises shown below 4 times before moving on to the next one and try and do them frequently throughout the day.

1 Lean against a wall with your knees straight and your heels on the ground and then maintain a good stretch for 20 seconds.

2 Next place your uninjured foot a stride length forward with both feet pointing forward, and gently go into a lunge position keeping the knee of the back leg straight and the heel on the floor. Again, hold the stretch for 20 seconds.

3 For the third stretch you will need a chair so that you can place the foot of the injured leg flat on the seat, with the back of your heel in line with the front edge of the chair. Push forwards trying to get your knee into contact with the back rest without raising your heel. Hold for 20 seconds.

4 Lastly, stand upright, feet flat on the floor and, without leaning forwards, allow your knees to bend. Hold for 20 seconds.

Achilles tendon pain – bursitis

How to identify

When you are looking for the origin of the Achilles tendon pain – first eliminate the areas which are not painful to the touch. These will be the neck of the tendon, and the upper part as it becomes muscular – called the musculotendinous junction. If these areas aren't painful on pressure then the part to examine is where the tendon inserts into the heel. If this area is tender to pressure, but is painless when rising on tip-toe, you can be fairly sure that the small sac of fluid behind the tendon has become inflamed – you have bursitis.

How to treat

Treatment is again different from the other two forms of achilles tendon pain that we have looked at. This time massage or frictions must NOT be used; in fact, every effort must be made to reduce pressure on the back of the heel. It is an inflammatory condition, so the use of ice is needed again – 3 times each day for 10 minutes, followed by the application of an anti-inflammatory cream. As in the treatment of other conditions, application in the morning, at tea time and just before going to bed gives a good spacing.

This condition can be caused by pounding on the heel when road running – in which case wearing shock absorbing heel inserts will be a big help. Sometimes the cause is not from running at all, but due to the back of the heel of your ordinary day-time shoes cutting in – they may be very rigid at the back, or have too great a curve so that the back of the shoe presses on the heel. It is possible to make a small insert from a piece of chiropody felt for the back of the shoe, to push the heel forwards slightly and reduce the pressure.

This is another condition, where you need to rest from running until the symptoms settle. This could well take two or three weeks, but at least you can cycle and do various forms of circuit training to keep your basic fitness.

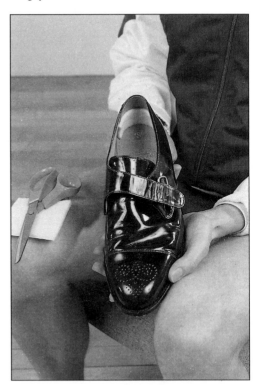

To treat bursitis, you may have to insert some chiropody felt in your ordinary day-time shoes.

Knee – chondromalacia patellae

How to identify

With the condition chondromalacia patellae runners complain of pain around the front of the knee but cannot locate the source of it exactly. It hurts when running, often when cycling, sometimes when walking and nearly always when running down stairs.

If you sit still for any length of time then the pain is worse when you get up to walk. Similarly with driving; when you get out of the car after a journey your knee has 'seized-up'.

If it looks as though you may be suffering from this condition then there are a couple of simple tests you can carry out on yourself to confirm it.

If you get pain on any of these tests then it looks as though you have chondromalacia patella – a softening and soreness behind the knee cap.

How to treat

You need to tackle this problem in two ways. Firstly treat the symptoms with an ice pack or, probably more conveniently if you don't have one, use a small bag of frozen peas and freeze them after each use.

Use the ice three times a day, morning, tea-time and just before going to bed is a pretty good spacing, and only leave the ice on for 10 minutes for maximum benefit. After using the ice put some anti-inflammatory cream on the area you found to be sore when you tested it.

As well as treating the symptoms you'll need to do something about strengthening

Knee – chondromalacia patellae test

1 Sit on the floor and let the muscles on the front of your thigh relax. Press down on your knee cap and tighten those muscles. Do this first with pressure straight down towards the floor, and if that is okay then angle the pressure first to one side and then to the other side.

2 Still sitting on the floor and with the muscles relaxed, push your knee cap across to one side and probe behind the edge with your finger to see if it is tender. If that's okay then try the other side.

159

the muscles in the front of your thigh – the quadriceps. With any problem in the knee these muscles quickly start to waste away and then you get imbalance in the two legs which then pulls the knee cap to one side and worsens the condition.

Unfortunately, with this condition, any exercise that uses the knee joint will make matters worse so you are stuck with only one exercise – straight leg raising. It's pretty boring but at least it's very effective, particularly if you do it as described below.

Apart from this exercise it's complete rest – no running, no cycling not even swimming until the symptoms have gone.

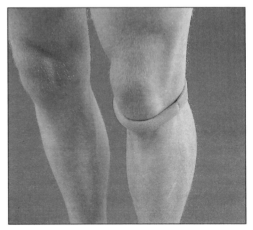

You can try strapping the affected knee throughout the day to relieve pressure on the knee cap.

If you're one of the unlucky ones and the problem is persistent or keeps coming back when you start running again, then try a strapping. Wear it throughout the day to relieve the pressure on the knee cap.

Usually if you can identify what has caused an injury, there is a fair chance that you can avoid it happening again, but it's not very easy with chondromalacia. A direct blow to the front of the knee can cause it but that's not very likely with runners. More likely is simple over-use, in which case try to be a bit more aware of the dangers when you are back in full training and at any sign of a recurrence treat the symptoms and start again with the straight leg raising.

Sometimes it can be just a weakness and imbalance in the quadriceps resulting from some other injury such as a sprained ankle, in which case once the straight leg raising has done its job there won't be any further trouble.

Straight leg raising

Tighten the muscles and raise the leg about 15cm/6 inches. Hold for a time, then relax for 10 seconds and repeat – do it 10 times altogether each session. Now as to the length of time that you hold your leg raised – build up until you can manage all 10 repetitions for 50 seconds – then you can add some weight and build up again.

Knee – patellar tendon

How to identify

Unlike chondromalacia patellae where the area of pain is rather vague, with the patellar tendon the pain is very specific, occurring on the lowest part of the knee cap.

There is no pain at rest, but it comes on with running or cycling or, in fact, with any strenuous use of the legs. The more strenuous the exercise, the worse the pain, so running up hills or steps is particularly bad and even walking may be painful for a time after such a training session. Kneeling is also very painful because it puts direct pressure right on the damaged area.

How to treat

This is the most common sort of trouble in this area and unfortunately it only seems to respond to an injection of prednisolone, so it means a trip to see your doctor to enlist his aid.

If you're a very patient person then prolonged rest can sometimes resolve it – but that isn't usually acceptable to runners.

Patellar tendon test

To test for this condition, sit on the floor with the muscles in the front of your thigh relaxed. Press very lightly on the top of the knee cap with one hand – this will lift the bottom of the knee cap very slightly. With one finger of the other hand press firmly right on the pole of the patella (if you have just been training hard then you may very well jump through the ceiling).

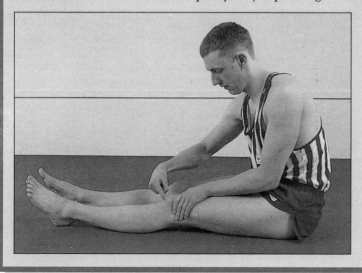

Shin splints

We are now going to look at a very common injury. It affects all types of runners – track, road or country. It's usually referred to as 'shin splints'.

How to identify

With this condition you will find that the pain is present all the time that you're running, not like some injuries where the pain appears to clear during the run.

At most other times there won't be any symptoms except perhaps if you squat fully

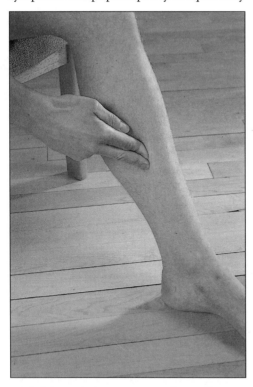

To find the precise area, press your fingers along your leg behind the edge of the shin bone.

so that you are sitting on your heels. If you have had the condition for a long time and have chosen to ignore it, then your leg is likely to be sore most of the time.

If you find that you have pain along the edge of your shin bone and this affects you when running but gives very little trouble at other times, then shin splints is the condition to consider first of all. Often this will affect both legs, but if so it does at least reduce the possibility of it being some other problem such as a stress fracture.

Sit with your knee bent to relax the calf muscle, then press your fingers along your leg just behind the edge of the shin bone to find the precise area.

How to treat

Once you have located it the treatment can begin.

● Stop running until the symptoms have cleared.

● Three times a day apply a cold pack for 10 minutes. A good way is to use a proprietary reusable hot/cold pack. Alternatively, wrap a single ice cube in a cotton handkerchief and gently massage over the affected area for 10 minutes.

By the way, the 10 minutes is important; don't get carried away and think that longer is better – it isn't. After the ice apply an anti-inflammatory cream – some are available from the chemist without a prescription. Don't forget these things need to be done three times a day – morning, tea-time and just before going to bed would be fine. Apart from treating the symptoms, try to find the cause of the problem.

It may simply be that you have been running more than usual on a hard surface – the solution is obvious – when you do start running again start on softer ground, and incidentally don't wear spikes until you are completely cured.

The most common cause is probably over-pronation. You can check for this by looking at the wear pattern of your running shoes – if over-pronation is the culprit then you will see greater wear on the inner edge of your shoes than on the outer edge.

If you find that this is the case then you have two options – you can buy running shoes specially designed to correct over-pronation or you can buy a pair of orthotics. These are specially designed inserts to go into your shoes and can be tailor-made for you but do tend to be rather expensive. A good alternative is to purchase a pair of rigid orthotics which are available from good sports shops.

With over-pronation, there is greater wear on the inner, not outer, edge of your shoes.

Most people find that this solves the problem and they can be worn during the day in your ordinary shoes as part of the treatment.

Whilst you have symptoms don't run at all, but cycling is fine and it does keep up your fitness. If after two or three weeks you are not significantly improved then you have to consider the possibility of a stress fracture. This means that a visit to your doctor is necessary and he will organise for you to have an X-ray.

Muscle tear

How to identify
With runners, muscle tears occur mainly in one of three areas:
1 The calf.
2 The front of the thigh.
3 The back of the thigh.

For the most part, tears happen very abruptly. There is a sudden sharp pain and you cannot carry on running. Just occasionally, however, there can be a slow onset where a slight strain is allowed to worsen.

How to treat
As soon as you feel the sharp pain of a torn muscle, follow the golden rule: get ice to the damaged area as soon as possible and as often as possible, but only for 10 minutes at a time and leave an hour between applications. This will reduce the

internal bleeding in the muscle and will substantially shorten the recovery time. Apply some compression to the muscle between the applications of ice. The other thing to remember is to rest with the leg raised as much as possible during the first 24 hours.

Two days later you can start treatment – this will be in the form of heat, massage and stretching. The heat is best applied by using a hot water bottle on the affected area for 15 minutes at least once a day.

Luckily the three areas likely to be affected can all be reached for massage by yourself and whilst it won't be as effective as that from a physiotherapist, it will certainly help. In each case the massage needs to be fairly deep and across the muscle fibres. But a timely word of warning here – if your calf pain was not caused when you were actually running or doing an activity, then DON'T treat it yourself – and especially don't massage the muscle as the cause may not be a torn muscle. Instead seek professional advice from your doctor.

Self massage

To massage the calf, the muscle can be relaxed by sitting with your knee bent. This same position is also suitable for massaging the hamstrings which are the muscles at the back of the thigh. To massage the quadriceps, which are on the front of the thigh, the leg must be kept straight.

Now for stretching. Remember to always stretch slowly and without any bouncing. Hold each stretched position for about 20 seconds.

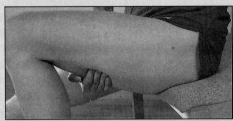

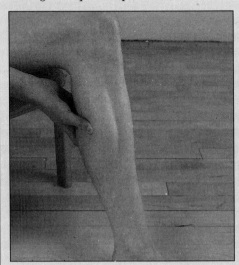

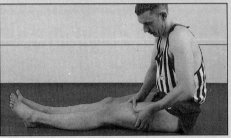

Calf stretches

For the calf there are five good exercises that can be done.

1 Stand facing a wall and about 3 feet away from it. Place your hands against the wall, keeping your knees straight and your heels on the floor. By regulating the amount by which you bend your arms the degree of stretching in your calf can be controlled. There will be some discomfort as you stretch the injured muscle; this is fine but don't force it too much, particularly during the first 2 or 3 days.

2 The starting position is simply to stand upright (below). Take a short stride forwards with your good leg, keeping the injured leg straight with the heel on the ground. The length of stride will dictate the amount of stretch achieved. When you can manage a good length stride, then further stretching can be obtained by bending the knee of your leading leg and getting into the lunge position.

3 This exercise produces a much more severe stretching so is best reserved for use after a few days practising the first two exercises. Stand facing any upright surface and trap the foot of your injured leg against that surface. Even greater stretching can be achieved by pushing yourself closer to the upright surface.

4 Stand upright, then without leaning forwards, slowly bend your knees, keeping your heels flat on the ground.

5 Finally, place the foot of your injured leg on a kitchen chair so the heel is in line with the front edge. Now push your knee forwards bringing it as close as possible to the back rest but keeping your heel down.

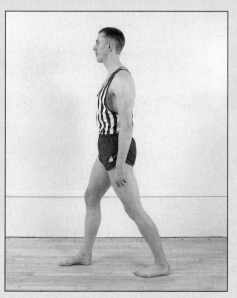

Hamstring stretches

For the hamstrings we have three good stretching exercises.

1 *Lying flat on your back, loop a strap or towel around the foot of your injured leg. Keep your legs straight and, using both hands, pull the strap or towel towards you, thus raising your leg.*

2 *Sit on the floor, keeping your injured leg straight out in front of you and bending your good leg. Lean forwards to grasp your ankle, and by pulling yourself towards your ankle you will produce a strong stretch in the hamstring muscle.*

3 *Prop the heel of your injured leg up on a solid surface such as a chair or table. Keep your leg straight and lean forwards to grasp your ankle. The amount of stretching can be gradually increased over a period of a few days by progressively increasing the height of the surface.*

Quadriceps stretches

For the quadriceps you will only need these stretching exercises.

1 Stand upright and take hold of the ankle on your injured leg. Steady yourself with your free hand and pull your foot up to your buttock until you feel pain in the damaged muscle. When you are able to bring your heel right up, further stretching can be achieved by pulling your leg back.

2 Kneel and sit back on your heels. More stretching is obtained by progressively lying further and further back.

These procedures will have to continue for about 10 days or until the symptoms have gone, but after about three days of treatment, rehabilitation can begin.

Start by putting on a track suit and trainers, going for a 30-minute walk and occasionally breaking into an easy jog for about 50 metres. Increase the amount of running until after a few days you will be running slowly for the full 30 minutes. Now the run can become a fast and slow session, but still well below full speed.

Next progress to some turnabouts. Run at a fast stride for 100 metres on the flat, take a 15-second rest and run back. Take another 15-second rest and run back again, until you have done eight runs.

When you can handle this work-out without trouble then you can make a progressive return to your normal training. Whilst the time scale will vary with the severity of the tear, the overall pattern remains the same – just don't get impatient.

Back problems

How to identify

Although sometimes spinal problems can be felt as pain, aching or stiffness in the back itself, far more commonly back-related problems, are felt as a referred pain elsewhere in the body. This is often in the form of sciatica – pain down the back of the thigh, or it may be pain or aching in the buttock, hip, knee or even the foot. You may find that there isn't even any associated back pain – sometimes there isn't. Because of this it can be difficult to diagnose back trouble but there are one or two clues. If you have a persistent injury which appears to clear up with rest and treatment but then returns each time you get into training again, start looking at the possibility of it being back related. Also if it's difficult to locate or identify the pain despite carrying out the checks for specific conditions described throughout this chapter, then again that suggests back trouble.

With runners, back problems are nearly always caused by compaction of the spine due to the impact of repeated foot strike. This causes the disc between the vertebrae to be compressed and distorted, eventually coming into contact with a nerve root, so causing the referred pain.

How to treat

Overcoming the problem has two aspects – reducing the distortion of the disc and reducing the cause of the distortion.

There are two very effective exercises to mobilize the spine and so start to correct the distortion. Both these exercises are best done lying on the bed, so ideal times to do them are first thing in the morning and last thing at night whilst the symptoms are severe, though they can be done more frequently. These exercises are very simple but *don't* underestimate them – they are very effective.

Spine mobilization exercises

1 For the first exercise, lie flat on your back, if wished with a pillow for your head. Then, without raising your legs or bending your knees, lengthen and shorten your legs – all the movement coming from your hips. Continue to do this, with maximum range of movement, continuously for one minute.

2 Stay on your back for the second exercise, but this time have your knees bent. Without letting your shoulders move, rock your legs from side to side, keeping your feet and knees together. You should be able to touch down with your knees, first to one side and then the other. Work at this exercise continuously for one minute.

In addition to mobilizing the spine it is also very effective to take up a resting position designed to flatten the spine, thereby reducing the compression on the disc. To do this, lie on your back with your legs propped on a piece of furniture so that you take up a Z-shape. As you relax you will find that the curvature of your spine lessens until your back is flat and supported by the floor – to be effective you will need to remain in this position for at least 15 minutes.

A more positive way to reduce the compression on the disc is to apply

This resting position is good for flattening the spine and reducing compression on the disc. Lie on your back with legs supported by a chair. Slowly relax your spine until your back is flat on the floor. Hold this position for at least 15 minutes.

traction. That is a pulling action on the spine to replace the pressing action that you are getting all day due to gravity. The simplest way to apply traction is to hang from a beam or bar by your arms and let your body-weight do the pulling. Whilst in theory this sounds very easy in practice it's seldom possible to hang for long enough for it to be useful. A much better alternative is to use one of the proprietary traction units designed for home use. The one shown here is particularly good, as it is not only safe and easy to use but can be completely self administered.

It is a generally held belief that a very firm mattress is best for back sufferers but this is not always so. Most benefit from a firm base to the bed but with a very soft mattress on top. In fact mattresses that are soft enough don't appear to be made, so here is a good alternative. Take two or three spare duvets or eiderdowns and fold them double, place them on top of your

mattress under the bottom sheet and sleep on those. It should make a big difference.

Now on to ways of reducing the cause of the distortion. Running a high mileage on the roads is a major culprit and the remedy is fairly obvious. For the time being you have to cut down on the mileage and try to run on softer ground.

Because impact is your number-one enemy there are two other precautions you must take. Wear shock-absorbing heel inserts at all times, both in your running shoes and in your day shoes. Avoid running downhill until you are cured. This is bad news for you fell runners in particular, but not only is there a tremendous increase in impact in running downhill but the spine is placed into extension at the same time, adding to the risk.

If despite trying all this advice the problem won't go away then it really is essential to get professional help – go to see a qualified physiotherapist.

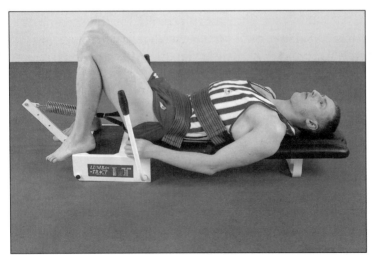

You can buy traction units for home use to reduce the compression on the disc. This type is simple to use and very effective.

Road racing –
the new distances

by Cliff Temple

Every weekend thousands of runners take part in road events at two distances which until relatively recently were not even part of the athletics programme: the 10km and the half-marathon (21.1km)

These distances, now so quickly and thoroughly established, became the filling in the sandwich out of necessity and public demand, seized upon by many runners who felt they were not fast enough for the track, but did not want to keep turning out in full marathons.

Yet in the early 1980s, when the running boom developed, the two best supported events in Britain were at opposite ends of the spectrum, with no such middle ground. One was the Sunday Times National Fun Run which attracted, at its peak, around 30,000 runners of all ages to run a flat grassland course of just 4km (2½ miles) around Hyde Park each September. The other was the London Marathon, which began in 1981, and soon attracted around 70,000 entries for its 25,000 available places.

So when opportunities evolved for runners to take part in 10km and half-marathon events, the uptake was enormous, and a suitable bridge between

the two former islands of the fixture list was established. The National Fun Run still continues, though in more modest numbers, and the London Marathon is thriving.

However prior to the great upswing in running participation, club athletes had to rely on a series of traditional and scarce 5-mile and 10-mile races in their areas to suit their needs, and, from the sport's point of view, a great opportunity for long-standing clubs and hard-working officials to capitalize on their dedication over the years by going out to attract the new wave of runners was missed. Instead, the traditional British 5- and 10-milers remained relatively insular events, while the transatlantic influence (where the necessity for intermediate distances and the lack of traditional races in the wake of a similar marathon upsurge in the USA had already resulted in the development of a series of 10km and half-marathon races, usually with good commercial backing) was felt in the UK.

Eventually the British AAA established a national 10km championship following the success of so many regional races at the distance, while the flagship of the half-marathon has, since 1981, been the Great

North Run on Tyneside. Originally the brainchild of local north-east running hero Brendan Foster, its inaugural year of 1981 had 10,681 finishers, including a seven-year-old boy, but fortunately it later came under official AAA rules which imposed minimum age limits. Now each year it is swamped with applications for its 30,000 available places, and in 1992 staged the inaugural IAAF World Half-marathon championship in conjunction with the mass race – the final seal of approval that the distance itself had been internationally recognised.

The Great North Run is now one of Britain's most popular races, with a field of 30,000 runners.

However as the 10km and half-marathon are held on the road rather than the track, enormous care has to be taken that the courses are measured accurately and tremendous strides have been made in the art of course measurement in recent years.

Public participation

The particular interest in 10km and half-marathon participation has come from a number of different sources. For new runners, they represent logical steps up to an eventual marathon, and steps that were not so readily available to potential marathoners just a few years back. But, after all, if you cannot run 13 miles

comfortably, or even six, then what chance have you got at 26?

For those who went straight into marathons, hooked by the magic of the event, these shorter distances now provide a perfect alternative. Not only can they be used as part of marathon preparation, but for some athletes who want to put aside that stamina-draining event, at least for a while, they offer a similar experience of running camaraderie among masses of participants. Nor do they leave the same aching after-effects of a marathon, which means that such races can be tackled more frequently and without the interruption to normal running routine which marathon-recovery usually requires.

For newer runners, especially those with limited time, the prospect of completing a 10km event may be far more realistic than completing a marathon, and therefore much more of a motivation. The enormous success of a national series of 10km events has shown that it is a very popular distance for women runners at all levels, to whom it poses a worthwhile yet achievable challenge. But the 10km and the half-marathon can mean different approaches for different runners, according to their aims and ambitions.

The fun runner

For those whose targets in running are mainly, initially anyway, simply to start and finish a set distance in a reasonable state, with no major concern about position or time, the 10km is probably just

the next stage on from a 2-3 mile fun run. In mass 10km events, many of the runners are just aiming to finish, and by natural progression of a training programme of steady running the ability to cover 10km is open to practically anyone. A training pattern revolving around regularity of training, rather than bursts of activity followed by weeks of 'rest', is the path to success here, and while it may not be necessary to have run the full distance before the first race, the runner should have covered at least 4½ miles at the pace he expects to run in the race.

A continuation of the same routine, with a weekly 'long' run, is the preparation for a half-marathon too: the demands are the same, but they just go on for longer. So do not rush the jump from a successfully completed 10km to an attempt at the half-marathon, which is more than twice as long.

The would-be marathon runner

If your aim is to use the 10km and half-marathon as steps up to an eventual first marathon (for which they are well suited), you would be best advised to have run each distance at least two or three times in competition before trying the full marathon. Do not just run one 10km and think, "Well, that's that knocked off – now for the half-marathon!"

As a means of noting progress, a series of runs at 10km and half-marathon (as long as you ensure they are run on courses

173

Marathon preparation	
Week 1	– 10km race
Weeks 2-4	– Training
Week 5	– Easier training week, followed by second 10km race
Weeks 6-9	– Training
Week 10	– Easier training week, followed by half-marathon race
Weeks 11-13	– Training
Week 14	– Easier training week, followed by third 10km race
Weeks 15-17	– Training
Week 18	– Easier training week, followed by second half-marathon race
Weeks 19-21	– Training
Week 22	– Easy week
Weeks 23-25	– Training
Week 26	– Very easy week, followed by marathon

the following example of how to spread training and racing is suggested as a minimum for someone who, it is assumed, is a fairly fit runner and wants to run a marathon in six months' time.

The resting marathon runner

For those runners who started competition at marathon distances, the 10km and half-marathon may suggest that they are distances that are either (a) easy, or (b) a bit of a sprint. For the average marathon runner they are not really either of those, but they should be tackled as distances that do need to be run faster. A runner who covers the half-marathon in exactly half the time he normally takes for the marathon (or slower!) is certainly not getting the best out of himself.

Adapting to the needs of running faster requires forms of training other than the steady pace at which many people are content to run. The section from page 175 onwards outlines some of the possibilities of variety, although each runner will have to decide exactly what level of effort is required for him. The point is that while a great deal of steady-paced running will build stamina and improve cardiovascular fitness to a certain degree, for improvement in fitness to continue, the training loads placed on the body have to be graduated, too.

Since one logical extension of running 50 miles a week might theoretically be to run 500 miles a week it could be argued that just increasing sheer distance is one

that have been certified as accurately measured) can help you assess your development. But remember that it is virtually impossible to train hard and race well simultaneously, so you will need to allow an easy week before each race if it is to have any significance. On the other hand, you will need to allow some weeks (at least three) of harder training to bring about any significant improvement in your form. So you should plan well ahead, and way of adding to the load. I urge you to take my word that 500 miles a week is too much! And even if it were possible time-wise, it would leave you exhausted, slow and probably injured.

But by introducing faster runs at shorter distances, which push the pulse rate higher than reached in steady running, a significant improvement is possible. One by-product, incidentally, of preparing for 10km and half-marathons through the use of interval training,

In a 10km road race, an elite male runner will run at around 4½ minute pace, so speedwork is an important part of an athlete's training and race preparation for this event.

repetition training, fartlek and so on, is that if and when the runner does return to marathons in the future, he may notice a degree of improvement there, too. In fact, the section on how to break three hours for the marathon (see page 48) recommends faster running as the next stage on from saturation mileage.

Specific training for 10km

For a serious runner who wants to peak for a specific 10km road race, how should he plan his preparation? The main difference between 10km and, say, the marathon (apart from the distance) is the degree to

Weekly training schedule

Sunday		- 15-20 miles steady		400m jog recovery
Monday	am	- 5 miles steady		*or* 12 x 400m at track,
	pm	- 7 miles faster		with 200m jog recovery
Tuesday	am	- 5 miles steady	Friday	- 5 miles steady, or
	pm	- 6 x 1600m at track,		rest
		with 800m jog recovery	Saturday	am - 3 miles steady
Wednesday	am	- 5 miles steady		pm - RACE: Road relay of 3
	pm	- 10 miles fartlek, but		miles approximately or
		including 4 x 2		5 miles cross-country
		minutes hard at will		in winter. Track race
Thursday	am	- 5 miles steady		of 3000m or 5000m
	pm	- 8 x 600m at track, with		in spring

which additional oxygen is required. The marathon is said to be 99 per cent aerobic, which means that the body is using oxygen at roughly the same rate as it draws it in. But at 10km, that percentage drops to only 85-90 per cent aerobic, and 10-15 per cent anaerobic. In simple terms, as you have to run faster, so you get more out of breath!

A top-level male runner will cover each mile in a 10km race at around 4½ minute pace, and an equivalent level female runner at about 5 minute miling. To extend that pace to marathon terms, were it possible to continue at that rate, the male would finish in around 1 hour 58 minutes and the female in 2 hours 11 minutes, both well inside current world bests.

So there is a particular need to include a form of speedwork in the 10km preparation; more so than in the marathon.

And while the basic groundwork is still a great deal of steady state running, up to around 100 miles a week in the case of the serious runner, two or even three sessions a week of fast running are an integral part of 10km preparation too. A typical training schedule for an ambitious runner who has some years of solid distance running is shown above.

Specific training for the half-marathon

It is almost frightening to realise that when Moses Tanui of Kenya set his UK all-comers' best for the half-marathon in the 1993 British Great North Run, he was operating at a pace of around 4 minutes 35 seconds for the mile, for more than 13 consecutive miles. That is only a handful of seconds per mile slower than we have already noted as a world class pace for 10km – and this was more than twice as far! It is clear that there is really no hiding from speed in the half-marathon at that level.

So the sample training schedule shown below is not that much different from the 10km schedule, and is again intended for the more serious runner. The intervals are longer, but the requirements for the race are fairly similar.

The need to adapt to shorter, faster racing, especially after a long period of steady running through the winter, must not be overlooked, and a series of races designed to sharpen up for the main event should be decided. Such a string of races can be very effective if arranged in order of declining distance. For example, a 10-mile (i.e. over-distance) race some 8 weeks before the planned peak could be followed at regular intervals by races at 6-7 miles across country, 5 miles on the road, road relay legs of 2½ - 3 miles, and finally a couple of low-key track races at, say, 3000m and 1500m a week or so before the big day.

The actual distance of 10km is perhaps best avoided, at least close to the peak, so that the runner can go into the event sharp, optimistic and with no preconceived idea of limitations formed by a too-recent excursion at the same distance. The track distance of 10,000m is best avoided too, because its own specific mental and physical demands do not necessarily generate a free spirit for road running the same distance. On the road the various inclines and declines allow a change of

Sample training schedule

Sunday		- 15-20 miles steady
Monday	am -	5-7 miles steady
	pm -	7-10 miles harder
Tuesday	am -	5 miles steady
	pm -	5 x 2000m, with 5 minutes recovery, *or* 6 x 1200m, with 600m jog recovery
Wednesday	am -	5-7 miles steady
	pm -	10 miles hilly run, with 4 bursts of 3 minutes hard at will

Thursday	am -	5 miles steady
	pm -	4 x 600m on track, alternating with 4 x 400m. 400m recovery walk/jog after each
Friday		- 5 miles steady, or rest
Saturday	am -	5 miles steady
	pm -	RACE: 10km road or 5/6 miles cross-country in winter. Track: 3000m or 5000m in spring or summer

Here the great Kenyan runner Moses Tanui is shown pounding the road in the 1993 British Great North Run. Running at a pace of around 4 minutes 35 seconds for the mile for 13 consecutive miles, he set a new UK all-comers best for the half-marathon.

muscle group here, a brief respite there, whereas to slog round the 25 identical laps too soon beforehand can merely serve to remind the runner how far it seems when the lap marker says "17 to go".

For women, the 10,000m track event is still relatively new anyway, but the IAAF briefly encouraged the inclusion in the calendar of a world championship road race for women only, first at 10km and later at 15km. Finally, logic prevailed, and it was increased to the half-marathon in 1992, when its winner was, appropriately, Liz McColgan, who was also reigning world track 10,000m champion at the time.

This sort of training is, naturally, quite fatiguing when carried on for a considerable period, and it is essential that in the final week or two before the major race of the season, it is reduced in volume, by cutting down on the amount of intervals and perhaps eliminating the morning runs on alternate days. That way the body gets some additional recovery time in which to repair itself and recuperate. Normally there are just not enough days in the week to include the essential training, rest and racing before the whole pattern starts again.

A steep reduction of work can have a significant effect, though probably only two or three times a year, and it is important to save those occasions where possible to coincide with a major race. Quite often an athlete returning from injury, with a short but enforced reduction in training, will show improved form in the succeeding weeks. But this is almost certainly due to the cumulative effect of months of hard training followed by the rest. To merely reduce all training – as long as it was pitched at the right level in the first place! – would simply lead to an eventual drop in form anyway.

In the final week, a reduction of the interval session on Thursday prior to the race could be simply to run 1 x 600m and 1 x 400m, keeping the sharpness of running fast without the fatigue of doing so repeatedly. The feeling of being fresh but quick is the one elusively sought by every athlete before every event!

Racing-wise, the runner building up to a half-marathon in which he wants to perform well can use the race sequence of declining length similar to the 10km pattern. A 10-miler six weeks before the race can be followed by a 10km road race, a 5-mile cross-country race, a 3-mile road relay leg or 5000m track race, and perhaps finishing with a 3000m or 1500m low-key track race the week before the 'peak'. Most successful runners have a certain pride and dignity which occasionally works against them, as when they are sometimes reluctant to take part in an under-distance race in which they feel they might be 'shown up', even though they know it is good for their preparation for their main goal of the season.

Someone who overcame that feeling most successfully was Brendan Foster, perhaps Britain's most successful athlete of the 1970s and a runner who, had he not retired when he did, could possibly have become as great a runner on the roads as his contemporary Carlos Lopes. In 1974, after he had already broken the world 3000m record on the track, Foster completed his preparations for that summer's European 5000m championships with an 800m in which he finished only

fifth, and a 400m in which he finished dead last, five seconds behind the winner. But he knew the value of what he was doing in search of sharpness, and several weeks later he won the European title with one of the most comprehensive victories seen in the event. The principle is the same, even if the race for which you are

A typical week's training for a half marathon

Sunday		- 15-20 miles steady
Monday	am	- 5-7 miles steady
	pm	- 7-10 miles harder
Tuesday	am	- 5 miles steady
	pm	- 5 x 2000m, with 5 minutes recovery, *or* 6 x 1200m, with 600m jog recovery
Wednesday	am	- 5-7 miles steady
	pm	- 10 miles hilly run, with 4 bursts of 3 minutes hard at will
Thursday	am	- 5 miles steady
	pm	- 4 x 600m on track, alternating with 4 x 400m. 400m recovery walk/jog after each
Friday		- 5 miles steady, or rest
Saturday	am	- 5 miles steady

preparing is considerably longer and the standard considerably lower.

Foster, incidentally, used to define a distance runner as someone who woke up tired and went to bed even more tired.

Summary

It seems certain that fields for the 10km and half-marathon events will become bigger still in future years. That is reassuring, because it means that many new runners are having a more comfortable baptism into the sport than the majority of their predecessors who went straight to marathons. And for those who did, there is the realisation that they can enjoy the competition and challenge of shorter events far more often than the marathon.

One newcomer in 1984 ran more marathons in his first year of competition than a very experienced clubmate of his had done in nearly 25 years of distance running. The significant difference was that the newcomer was getting slower with each one he ran; the more cautious old-timer was still getting faster!

The 10km race has become the most popular road race in the world, especially in the United States. It attracts runners of all standards – from the elite athletes and club runners to fun runners who often like to attempt this distance before tackling a marathon. The AAA 10km race is shown here.

Racing and competition

by Steve Smythe

Few sportsmen or women will ever play soccer with Gazza at Wembley, tennis against Graf at Wimbledon, golf with Nick Faldo at the Masters, or box against Lennox Lewis at Las Vegas. However, most club athletes have competed against the very best runners at some of the biggest events or venues. Thousands of average runners who compete in marathons run alongside the world's best athletes.

For instance, the runners in the 1992 Great North Run in the UK were able to say they were up against all the brilliant Kenyans who were taking part in the World Half-marathon Championships, held in conjunction.

Even in events away from big championships, I personally have run in the same road race as Steve Cram, Steve Ovett and Sebastian Coe or, further back in time, track races against world record holders Brendan Foster and Dave Bedford. All these were open events and anyone could have lined up and, at least for a few seconds, say they were up against the very best.

Running is also unique in how it quantifies success. If you play a football match, you either win, lose or draw.

However an event like a marathon doesn't have one winner and all the rest losers. Each runner has a goal, whether it is sub 2:20, three hours or five hours or just to finish, and if they achieve that then they can regard themselves as winners too.

One of the joys of running is how easy it is to evaluate your success and improvement. A footballer may think he's had a good game but unless he's scored, would find it difficult to quantify any improvement. However, a runner's performance is timed to the second (or less if it's a track race), and it's easy to tell whether or not he or she has had a good competition.

People with experience from other sports are usually surprised at the good fellowship demonstrated even in the heat of serious competition. This is because, apart from at the very sharp end of the field where runners' livelihoods may depend on the outcome, most runners consider they are competing against the clock, distance or the course rather than their fellow men or women.

However, man is a competitive animal and for those runners who want to work hard and dedicate themselves to a goal and

compare their performances against others, then the sport of running has an ideal competitive structure. However, it does not have to be cut-throat and you will be surprised at the encouragement you'll get from your fellow competitors. Runners, whatever their standard, share a common goal and respect the efforts of all people who line up with them.

The competitive structure

The competitive structure varies throughout the world from country to country, but Britain has one of the oldest and also one of the most comprehensive so it is a good model to study. Whatever your level, or your favourite surface or distance, there should be an event for you.

Marathons are an opportunity for runners of all ages and abilities to compete: against each other or themselves! These runners are passing the Cutty Sark on the historic route of the London Marathon.

The man on the street may think the only races are those that he sees on the television, but each week there are probably over 100 different events taking place in Britain alone over a range of distances and surfaces.

Until the London Marathon's arrival in 1981, the UK structure was geared more to a good standard club athlete and there were far fewer events in which to participate. However, the marathon caused a great increase in interest and participants and many new events sprang up.

The new wave of runners also led to the creation of many new clubs, especially where the traditional Harrier clubs were not thought to be serving the needs of the newcomer. There are now thousands of different clubs to choose from. They offer the individual plenty of competition and even the clubs originally thought of as elitist will try to cater for all types and standards of runner.

Club membership

If you are going to compete in the UK, it is best to join a club. If you want to participate at cross-country or on the track there is little competitive opportunity for an unattached runner as the events are heavily club orientated. It is also against the BAF rules at these disciplines (but not the road) to compete for longer than 12 months as unattached.

Runners can compete in road races as unattached but you have to pay an additional small levy which goes towards the Area Association for administration.

Club membership is not expensive and if you are competing regularly on the road it makes economic sense to join a club. Apart from saving money, it should also improve your running. It will give you a competitive opportunity in events such as road relays and cross-country leagues. It will also provide you with training facilities, advice, coaches, company, social events and the presence of others of a similar standard.

If you want to find your nearest club, contact your Area Association who will advise you of suitable clubs relevant to the events in which you wish to compete.

There are thousands of clubs in Britain and many carry the title Athletic Club (AC). This implies that they run teams at all events: road all year, cross-country during the winter and track and field during the summer. Some clubs, however, are season-orientated or just interested in road running and cross-country (e.g. many clubs with 'Runners' in their title), and if you wish to compete in all areas of the sport, this may necessitate joining more than one club. Don't always go by the title, though. Even clubs with Joggers in their name may have started as jogging clubs, but now wholeheartedly enter teams in races and have some very quick club members.

While it should be easy to locate a club, finding out if it is right for you is more difficult. Before you join it is a good idea to go along a few times to see how you fit in and discover exactly what they have to offer. Some clubs try and cater for newcomers with beginners' sections but others may just not be suitable if you are a ten-minute miler.

Many athletic clubs are based at the local track and have an arrangement with a local authority for use of changing rooms and a clubhouse. The newer breed of running club, however, tends to meet at a park or local sports club or even a member's house.

Apart from geographically based clubs, there are also specialist clubs such as the Road Runners Club (RRC) and the 100Km Association for ultra runners. The RRC's aim is to 'to bring together all those interested in long distance running, to serve their interests, and to act as a forum for all enthusiasts'.

It has thousands of members and is an ideal organisation for the newcomer to road running to join for a modest annual subscription. Apart from extensive fixture lists, they also publish seasonal newsletters with plenty of road running information. In addition, they also have a standards scheme with awards given for achieving certain targets, with times adjusted depending on the severity of the course. These standards can act as a good incentive to improve.

Information and access

When an athlete is planning the new competitive season there are a number of sources of reference. There are club fixture cards, which tend to be published twice a year, winter and summer. In many clubs these would cater for the needs of most distance runners.

Further race information can be gathered from magazines, many of which publish extensive fixture lists each month with all the relevant information required to enter races directly. Some regional publications also provide race information on local events.

When competing at an event, you should also be able to find a good supply of future race entry forms available at the venue. While some organisers insist you enter on official entry forms, most will accept a standard form or even a written note as long as it is legible, contains your name, address, club, age or date of birth, the name of the event you are entering, confirmation that you are eligible under the rules of the BAF, and your signature. You will also need to enclose a stamped addressed envelope and a race fee.

Included in the fee will be a finishing medal, plaque or memento, and occasionally even a T-shirt. However, it is possible to get well organised but fairly basic events for a lot less. If you enter a major city marathon or half-marathon, expect to pay quite a lot more as they are more expensive to organise and require greater back-up.

The majority of events have an advertised closing date or an entry limit and stick rigidly to it. Other races are more relaxed and may even accept entries on the day, but will make an additional charge for this. However, if possible, enter well before the day. You will then be sure of your place, receive your number (if they are issued in advance) and all the necessary travel and race information. Runners who do enter on the day, apart from risking being turned away, cause race organisers a number of headaches in allocating resources such as medals, refreshments and, where there are computerized entries, cause delays in prizegivings and results.

There is quite often a charitable donation included in the entry fee and it is generally agreed that, compared to other sports, runners get good value from events and clubs.

Club fixtures

● **Cross-country**

The cross-country season runs from October to March in the UK and, apart from a few open events, most races are for club athletes only. Most clubs are affiliated to a winter league in which there will be between three and six fixtures a season.

There are numerous area and county leagues and nearly all of these leagues are open to any number of club members. They tend to be around five miles for the men and three miles for the women, with three to twelve club members counting in a scoring team. Most clubs have more than one team in a league so you do not have to be superfast to be a scorer.

Apart from the UK leagues, there are various championship races such as the County events in December, Area championships (Northern, Southern etc.) in January and the National events in late February or early March.

Although the addition of the World Cross-country trials has lessened the importance of the National event, where teams for the World Championships used to be selected, they remain a great sporting spectacle and very popular within the sport.

Every affiliated club can enter Area and National championships, whether they have a full team or not. The men's senior 'National' over 9 miles tends to attract around 2000 runners and clubs are restricted to just nine runners, of which six score. There are also races for Juniors (Under 20) and Youths (Under 17).

Cross-country races are a popular and well-supported part of the competitive scene in the UK. These seniors are competing in the men's National.

Clubs entered in the women's National can run as many runners as they wish of which four score, and there the entry tends to be around 600. There are also races for three younger age groups: Juniors (Under 20), Girls (Under 15) and Minor Girls (Under 13).

In addition to these events there are other regional championships (such as London, South of Thames, North of Thames, Bradford and District, Halifax and District) and various inter-club events and club championships.

Some of the above do have restricted entries so it is possible that if you are not in your club's top nine or dozen you may not get a chance to compete so often.

However, if your club does not require your services there are always plenty of road races to enter. There are certainly no restrictions in mob matches, which some of the oldest clubs still regard as a highly important part of the season. There, up to 100 members of each club can score, making everyone's position vital.

The average competitive club runner could find himself racing every week but it is far wiser to avoid injury and staleness by limiting your competitive outings to around once a fortnight.

● Track

There are more competitive opportunities for the non-club runner at track than cross-country thanks to the open graded meetings that normally take place monthly at a number of all-weather tracks during the summer. However, remember that you can run unattached for only a year.

The meetings usually include some sprint events, one middle-distance race (800m or 1500m) and a longer distance race (3000m or 5000m). The events are graded on runners, previous best performances, so that each race has runners' of a similar standard.

The events are ideal for the newcomer to try track racing without any pressure and as a gauge of progress. However, if you are going to try one, it is a good idea to have done at least some speed work on the track beforehand.

The meetings are well advertised in advance at the local track and in magazines.

These runners are racing along icy roads in the 9-mile Hog's Back road race in the UK. Road races vary enormously in the distances covered.

● **Road running**

It is on the road that an individual has the most freedom to race and the greatest competitive opportunities. While, many years ago, road races tended to fill the gaps between the cross-country and track season, there are now events on the road throughout the year, so if you don't enjoy running on the country or track you can limit your competitive outings to the road, and still race all year round.

The peak time for races is during the spring and autumn, when there can be almost 100 different races each weekend. While cross-country races tend to be on a Saturday, most road events take place on a Sunday morning, to avoid traffic.

Road races can range in distance from one mile to 100K (62 miles) but the most popular and common events are over 10K (6.2 miles) and Half-marathon (13.1 miles). Most races tend to be standard distances to enable you to compare performances but courses can vary greatly in difficulty. Not all events make comparison easy though. The Hog's Back race, near Guildford, England, which regularly attracts around 2000 runners, is over a route of just over nine miles. Two other events that have also been going well over 30 years are the Morpeth to Newcastle race on New Year's Day, which is 14.25 miles, and January's Mitcham 25K (15.5 miles).

One popular area of road racing in Britain is the relay. These events are guaranteed to generate excitement and provide an opportunity to cheer on clubmates. The leading relay in the country is the Men's National 12-stage in April over alternate three and six mile legs. Qualification for the event is through the Area 12-stage relays, a few weeks earlier. There are also National six-stage relays, women's national relays over three legs of around three miles, and a number of open events.

For those who want to try something different, away from the roads without resorting to a cross-country race, there are an increasing number of multi-terrain races. These are events that do not stick exclusively to the road and can be run over a variety of surfaces, such as grass, tracks and woodland paths. The distances are usually further than a typical cross-country race but because of the variety of surfaces, times are impossible to compare. Because of the difficult terrain there is often more camaraderie amongst competitors than in the average road race.

● **Fell racing**

A popular branch of running is fell or hill racing, which normally takes place in northern England, Scotland and Wales. It is not a sport recommended to the newcomer and should really be undertaken after a few years' experience of running on the road. Most races have a gruelling climb up mountains and then sharp descents and are not for the faint hearted!

This branch of the sport is run in Britain by the Fell Runners' Association (FRA) on behalf of the BAF. If you wish to take part in fell racing events in England and Wales, you will need to join the FRA.

Fell racing is one of the toughest and most gruelling forms of competitive running and is only for the most fit and experienced of runners. However, it is popular and attracts large fields of competitors.

When you do, for a fairly modest fee, you will receive a great deal of fixture information and an extensive magazine covering the sport. The FRA classifies its events to show how tough they are, depending on their distance and gradient. Therefore, if in the fixture lists, it states an event as 10m/1000 ft, this means the event is 10 miles long and involves 1000ft of climbing.

● Fun runs

In recent years, there have been a growing number of fun runs. These present a perfect opportunity for runners to ease their way into the competitive scene. The fun runs are more relaxed and less competitive than normal races and all runners should receive the same award, irrespective of finishing position (e.g. medal or certificate). Often they are held alongside an officially sanctioned race. Thus, while Mum or Dad are taking part in a half-marathon, their less competitive partner could be running slowly over 3K with son and daughter, still enjoying competing and receiving a memento for their efforts.

Planning a race programme

For many runners the sole reason they train is to compete. Others like to race as a change from just running by themselves to give them a good idea of their current fitness. Whatever your motivation, if you want to race seriously there are some important points to bear in mind.

These would include having a few easier days leading up to the race so that at least you start the event feeling fresh and raring to go rather than tired and wishing you were somewhere else. Different runners have different pre-race routines. Some like to have the day before the race completely free from running, others like to have a little jog and a few strides while others feel they must do a reasonably quick training run the day before to make sure they can still run quickly!

Others like to visualize how it will feel in the race and try and psych themselves up, especially if it is a race that they feel is especially important and for which they have been trying to peak.

It is not possible, of course, to peak continually and it is a good idea to choose your races many months in advance. You should then aim to gradually increase the training up until around three weeks before the big day, when the training quantity should be reduced but with increased emphasis on faster running, before easing back in the final week.

It is also a good idea to choose your races carefully leading up to the event at which you are aiming. For instance, if you were aiming to run well in a Half-marathon, you could run a 10-miler four weeks before and then a 5-miler to sharpen up a couple of weeks before the event.

With so much competitive opportunity it is important not to over-race, especially if you tend to concentrate on longer distances. A good rule of thumb is one day's rest from racing for every mile competed. So, if you run a marathon (26 miles), it will be nearly four weeks before you should compete again. Similarly, if you have run a half-marathon, wait two weeks before you next compete, whereas a 10K race could mean you may be able to race unscathed the following week.

Planning for race day

To get the best out of yourself on the day of the race, think about your requirements well in advance. This could mean making a list of all your kit and other essentials that you will be taking and clarifying travel arrangements and any meeting points with team-mates or supporters either before or after the event.

Rather than leave it to the last minute, pack your bag the night before, checking that your gear is in good condition and remember to take spare warm clothing or wet-weather gear and a towel and soap. All the kit and shoes should be tried and tested and comfortable.

If you have to register before the race, make sure you allow plenty of time for travelling, queueing and changing. At some races you may need to register for the event a day or two before, which may mean travelling prior to race day. This, at least, reduces the travelling time on race day and means you can have the psychological advantage of looking at parts of the course.

Thinking well ahead on all the aspects, will make it easier on the day and ensure you get the best out of yourself in the race.

The race plan

Your race plan should be carefully worked out depending on your current state of fitness, the quality of the opposition and weather conditions. Unless it is extremely hot or you are running a very long distance, it is important to warm up properly before the race. This should include some gentle jogging, some quicker running, a few strides (100m bursts at race pace to loosen up) and some relaxed, easy stretching.

If you are an inexperienced runner do not get carried away by the excitement of racing and start too fast. It is best to try to restrain yourself so instead of grinding to a halt in the later stages, you will be passing runners who misjudged their early pace. It is certainly more fun overtaking than being passed! If you do finish with plenty in hand, then at least you know you can run a little faster next time.

In some cross-country races or in narrow starts, it is necessary to start fast to avoid bottlenecks and queueing. However, once the initial rush has passed, ease back to a pace that you know you can maintain to the finish.

Competing internationally

One of the fastest growing aspects of competition is the growing number of opportunities to race abroad. There are now hundreds of overseas events, and they can be an ideal way of combining your racing, a holiday and some travel.

The most popular event is the New York Marathon, but other events, such as the Boston, Las Vegas, Los Angeles and Disney Marathons, are also attracting a growing international contingent For those who cannot afford America, there are also a number of European alternatives, such as races in Paris, Berlin, and Majorca.

Whilst it is possible to arrange your own travel, it is far easier to contact a specialist tour company. These organisations have been to the events before and will make all the necessary arrangements for you and it is much more fun travelling in a group. For those who are not quite ready to race, the tour companies also arrange training holidays in a wide range of locations such as Portugal and Lanzarote, and these are also growing in popularity.

Tactical tips

● Do not always lead your group as you will find it is easier to follow and you may get shelter from the wind. It is always easier to race with another runner's company as long as you are not straining unduly to stay with them.

● Practise relaxation and concentration. If you strain too much, you will eventually tire faster and when the race becomes tougher, especially in the second half, it is important to concentrate hard. Remind yourself of your training and the sacrifices and keep telling yourself to 'concentrate' and to 'keep pushing'.

● Most races have either mile or kilometre marks and whilst they are not always entirely accurate, it is a good idea, especially if you are an inexperienced runner, to check your pace to see if it is close to your pre-race plan.

● Set yourself a difficult but achievable target. It will give you an extra incentive to keep going and even if you don't quite reach it, you will at least have the satisfaction of having done your best.

Useful addresses

British Athletic Federation
225a Bristol Road,
Edgbaston
Birmingham
Tel: 021440 5000

Midland Counties AA
Edgbaston House
3 Duchess Place
Hagley Road
Birmingham B16 8NM
Tel: 021 452 1500

North of England AA
Suite 106
Emco House
5/7 New York Road
Leeds LS2 7PJ
Tel: 0532 461835

South of England AA
Suite 36
City of London Fruit
Exchange
Brushfield Street
London E1 6EU
Tel: 071 247 2963

Northern Ireland AAF
House of Sport
Upper Malone Road
Belfast BT9 5LA
Tel: 0232 381222

Scottish Athletics Federation
Caledonia House
South Gyle
Edinburgh EH12 9DQ
Tel: 031 317 7320

Athletics Association of Wales
Morfa Stadium
Landore
Swansea
West Glamorgan
SA1 7DF
Tel: 0792 456237

Specialist Clubs

Barrier Club (Steeplechase)
C. Elliott
1593B London Road
Norbury
London SW16 4AA

British Marathon Runners Club
Dr T. Smith
Green Pastures
Sheepcroft Lane
Whitemoor Holt
Wimborne
Dorset BH21 7DA

British Milers Club (800m-5000m)
M. R. Rezin
4 Russell Way
Winnersh
Nr. Wokingham
Berks RG11 5SN

Combined Events Club
G. Whall
63 Portsdown Road
Halesowen
W. Midlands B63 1HT

Hammer Circle
M. J. Morley
38 Leeds Road
Mirfield
West Yorks WF14 0DA

Kangaroo Club (Long and Triple Jump)
D. J. Hayward
Oakdene
The Old Rectory
Lowe Hill Road
Wem
Shropshire SY4 5UA

Road Runners Club
J. Legge
21 Station Road
Digswell
Welwyn
Herts AL6 0DU

UK Pole Vault Association
J. Evans
52 Cranmer Avenue
Ealing
London W13 9SH

British Athletics Supporters Club
11 Railway Road
Newbury
Berks RG14 7PE

International Athletes Club
66 Clerkenwell Road
London EC1M 5PX

National Union of Track Statisticians
2 Chudleigh Close
Bedford
MK40 3AW

British Olympic Association
1 Wandsworth Plain
London SW18 1ET
Tel: 081 871 2677

Schools Associations

English Schools AA
26 Newborough Green
New Malden
Surrey KT3 5HS

Scottish Schools AA
11 Muirfield Street
Kirkcaldy
Fife KY2 6SY

Ulster Schools AA
c/o Belfast Royal
Academy
Cliftonville Road
Belfast BT14 6JL

Welsh Schools AA
Neuadd Wen
Tref Eglwys Road
Llanidloes
Powys SY18 6JA

International addresses

Australia
Athletics Australia
PO Box 1400
North Melbourne
3051 Victoria Australia

Canada
Athletics Canada
1600 James Naismith
Drive, Gloucester
Ontario K1B SN4
Canada

New Zealand
Athletics New Zealand
PO Box 741
Wellington
New Zealand

South Africa
Athletics SA
PO Box 1261
Pretoria 0001
Republic of South
Africa

USA
The Athletics Congress of the USA
PO Box 120
Indianapolis
Indiana 46206-0120
USA

Index